Technology
for Motor Mechanics

PART 2   Vehicle and Electrical Technology

Technology
for Motor Mechanics

PART 2 (FIRST YEAR) Vehicle and Electrical Technology

SECOND EDITION

S. C. Mudd, F.I.M.I., A.M.B.I.M., A.M.A.E.T.

Senior lecturer in charge of Vehicle Courses
Huddersfield Technical College

Edward Arnold

© S. C. MUDD 1972

First published 1968
by Edward Arnold (Publishers) Ltd
25 Hill Street
London W1X 8LL

Second edition 1972

ISBN: 0 7131 3273 6

Filmset and printed offset litho in Great Britain by
Cox & Wyman Ltd
London, Fakenham and Reading

Preface to the Second Edition

This book is intended primarily to help the younger apprentices engaged in all the various trades involved in motor vehicle service and repair work. It has been revised to meet the requirements of the Part One syllabuses in Motor Vehicle Technology for the Motor Vehicle Craft Studies Examinations held by the City and Guilds of London Institute, and the Regional Examining Bodies.

The material provided has been deliberately widened in scope from the bare syllabus in the hope that it will assist in the co-ordination with other subjects and be of more interest to the young apprentice. It should also be of considerable help in the early stages of the Vehicle Technician Course.

Much emphasis has been placed on the use of simple diagrams in describing the construction and principles of the various units and systems. It is hoped that these diagrams, and the arrangement of the subject matter, will enable teachers and instructors to consider the book suitable for class use, and that such use, by reducing the amount of dictation and/or handout material, will enable much more class time to be devoted to the real work of teaching.

Huddersfield   S. C. MUDD
1972

Acknowledgements

The author wishes to express his grateful thanks for the advice and active assistance so generously given by his colleagues, and by the following companies:

The Chrysler Car Company
The British Leyland Motor Corporation
Citroën Cars
V.W. Motors Ltd
The Lockheed Brake Co
Girling Ltd
Joseph Lucas (Sales and Service) Ltd
C.A.V. Ltd
A.C.–Delco Division of General Motors
Electric Power Storage Ltd
Bork and Beck Ltd
Hardy Spicer Ltd
Laystall Engineering Co Ltd

Contents

ELECTRICAL TECHNOLOGY

1 The Layout of the Vehicle

The conventional motor car is a complex assembly which is composed of the following main units and systems:

(1) The chassis or frame.
(2) The body.
(3) The suspension system.
(4) The power unit.
(5) The transmission system.
(6) The braking system.
(7) The electrical system.

The chassis, Figs. 1.4, 2.1 and 2.2

This structure is the frame or skeleton of the car. Its function is to act as a mounting for all the other units and assemblies. It must also keep them in their correct relative positions in spite of all the varying loads to which they may be subjected. The chassis must be strong and rigid, and so shaped that it will not cause undue complication to the design and operation of the other assemblies. It is usually made from steel pressings which are welded or riveted together, reinforcing being added where necessary. The shape of the chassis will be determined by the type of suspension system used and by the location of the power unit.

The body

The body (Fig. 2.4) is made from a large number of steel pressings which are welded together. Together with the doors and boot it forms a weather-proof and comfortable compartment for the driver and passengers. The body is bolted to the chassis at numerous points but it adds little or no strength to the assembly. The wings in this type of chassis–body combination are usually separate pressings which are bolted on after assembly.

The suspension system

The function of the suspension system (Fig. 1.1) is to reduce, as far as is practicable, the amount of shock and vibration transmitted from the road wheels to the chassis and body. Modern systems employ coil springs for the front wheels and leaf springs for the rear wheels, but many different arrangements are possible and are in use.

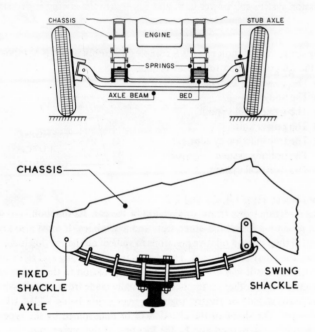

Fig. 1.1   Suspension arrangement (front)

The power unit

This includes the engine and the systems essential to its operation, i.e. radiator for cooling, fuel, ignition system and lubrication. The function of the engine is to convert the heat energy, contained in the petrol, into mechanical energy in the form of torque, or turning power, available at the engine crankshaft.

The transmission system

This includes the clutch, gearbox, propeller shaft, final drive, and rear axle case and half-shafts. The function of the transmission system is to transfer the torque available at the crankshaft to the driving road wheels, the size of the torque and the speed of the half-shafts being modified by the driver's use of the gearbox to suit the loads acting against the engine. Fig. 1.2(a) illustrates the main parts of the transmission system and power unit, and Fig. 1.2(b) the energy conversion.

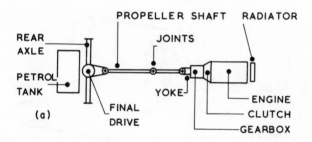

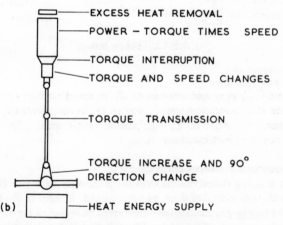

Fig. 1.2   Power and transmission: (a) arrangement of power unit and transmission; (b) conversion of energy

The braking system

This includes the actual brake assembly fitted at each road wheel and the system used for their operation (see Fig. 1.3). The function of the braking system is to retard or stop the motion of the car in either direction. The system must operate quickly and smoothly, and not pull the car to one side. The system operates by converting the movement energy of the vehicle into heat, via friction, and dissipating or getting rid of the heat to the cooling stream of air passing under the vehicle. The brakes may be activated by mechanical or fluid systems.

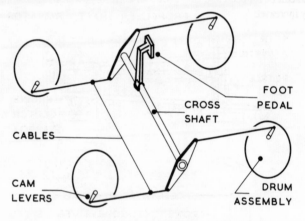

CROSS SHAFT

FOOT PEDAL

CABLES

CAM LEVERS

DRUM ASSEMBLY

Fig. 1.3 Simple brakes

The electrical system

This is used to supply and control all the electrical energy needed to operate the many electrical units fitted to the car to increase its use, convenience, and comfort, e.g. ignition for the engine, lights of all kinds, motors and battery charging.

Arrangement of components in the chassis

The chassis and body assembly is mounted upon axles (see Fig. 1.4). Wheels with tyres are fitted on to the axles. A form of springing is arranged between the axles and the chassis, as shown earlier in Fig. 1.1, and the violence of the spring rebound is absorbed or controlled by dampers or shock absorbers.

The engine, clutch and gearbox are bolted together, in their correct alignments, to form one large unit. This is mounted in the forward end of the chassis on rubber cushions which reduce the amount of vibration transmitted from the unit to the chassis and body.

The power produced by the engine is a combination of speed and torque. The gearbox is used to provide alternative combinations of speed and torque to match the varying loads imposed upon the engine by differing vehicle driving conditions. If the load acting against the engine becomes excessive, e.g. when climbing a steep hill, the vehicle speed can be reduced and the torque, or turning power, be correspondingly increased.

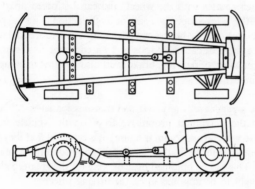

Fig. 1.4   Heavy car assembly

The clutch is used to interrupt the transmission of torque between the engine and the gearbox while the gear ratios are being changed, it being impossible to do this while the gear trains are under load.

The final drive assembly is mounted in the rear axle case and consists of a crown wheel and pinion gear assembly and a differential gear assembly. The function of the crown wheel assembly is to change the direction of the torque through 90°, i.e. to pass it from the propeller shaft to the half-shafts, and to effect a further reduction of speed and increase of torque which modifies the changes made by the gearbox. The differential gear assembly makes possible the difference in speeds between the half-shafts when the car negotiates a turn. It is so designed that although the half-shaft speeds may be different their driving torques remain the same.

The gearbox is mounted in the chassis while the final drive rises and falls with the rear axle. The propeller shaft is used to connect the two and it must therefore be fitted with a special joint at each end to permit these movements. As the axle follows an arc based on the forward shackle pin of the rear spring, the propeller shaft must also increase and reduce its effective length as it rotates. This is arranged by the use of the sliding joint which is usually combined with the forward universal joint.

The brake assembly at each wheel consists of two friction linings attached to steel shoes. These are mounted upon a fixed pivot secured to a fixed back-plate bolted to the axle. The shoes are enclosed by a drum, which rotates with the wheel, and can be forced apart by the action of either a lever-operated cam or by the action of a fluid pressure cylinder and piston. The brakes can be operated by a foot pedal working through a system of cables or rods or by a complete fluid system. An independent hand, or parking, brake must also be fitted to comply with legal requirements.

Alternative arrangements of power and transmission units

To obtain the maximum propulsive force on the vehicle from the driving road wheels (maximum traction), it is essential that they be kept in close contact with the road under all operating conditions (maximum adhesion). This can be obtained by arranging for the greater part of the vehicle weight to be imposed upon the driving wheels.

As far as cars are concerned two further points of design are important. The first is that of obtaining good road holding at high speeds and the second is that of passenger leg room and comfort. Good road holding is greatly assisted by bringing the centre of gravity of the whole vehicle closer to the ground; i.e. mounting all the heavier assemblies lower in the chassis and bringing the chassis closer to the ground. Extra leg room can be obtained by providing a flat floor – if the propeller shaft tunnel can be done away with.

With these three points in mind some car manufacturers have therefore produced vehicles in which the heavier units such as the engine, gearbox and final drive gears are mounted between the driving wheels and relatively close to the ground.

One of the best arrangements (from all points of view except possibly that of the cost of production until very large numbers are required) is the front-engine front-wheel drive. The greater proportion of the vehicle weight is always on the driving wheels, and the steering and suspension systems are not made unduly complicated. The space inside the body is not reduced by the necessity of making allowance for the fitting of a propeller shaft tunnel, and the chassis and floor can be

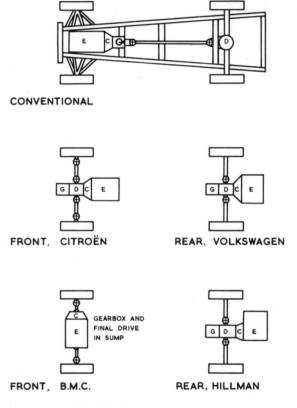

CONVENTIONAL

FRONT, CITROËN   REAR, VOLKSWAGEN

GEARBOX AND
FINAL DRIVE
IN SUMP

FRONT, B.M.C.   REAR, HILLMAN

Fig. 1.5   Engine positions: cars

brought closer to the ground. In these designs the front (driving) wheels are independently sprung and are driven by short shafts. The engine, gearbox and final drive gears are assembled as a unit and mounted in the forward end of the chassis. Examples of this arrangement are the

B.M.C. Mini Minor and 1100, the Saab, the Citroën, and the Renault 1500.

A number of Continental manufacturers, and a few British manufacturers, have produced rear-engine rear-drive vehicles.

The *advantages* claimed for this arrangement are:

(1) Excellent traction, especially when climbing hills.
(2) A very compact and accessible power and transmission assembly.
(3) A larger passenger space for a given length of body.

The *disadvantages* are that:

(1) There is a strong tendency for the vehicle to oversteer, i.e. tighten into a turn of its own accord.
(2) Space is wasted in the engine compartment while luggage space at the front has to be reduced to allow for the steering lock of the front wheels.

These disadvantages are much reduced by careful design, and successful examples of this arrangement of the engine and transmission are the Volkswagen, Simca 1000, Renault Dauphine, Chevrolet Corvair, and the N.S.U. Prinz.

Alternative front suspension

A number of vehicles have been produced in which a single leaf spring is used in the front suspension. In this arrangement the spring is inverted and secured in a channel section chassis crossmember by U-bolts. It is located in the cross-member by the head of the spring centre bolt. A beam axle is secured to the spring at each end by a special design of swinging shackle in which rubber is used to prevent excessive movement.

When a spring is fitted across the chassis in this manner it cannot resist the brake reaction forces, which tend to rotate the axle with the wheels, nor can it resist the driving and braking thrusts. Radius rods are therefore fitted from each axle end to meet at a ball joint mounted on the next chassis cross-member. These rods not only resist the thrust and reaction forces but also prevent the axle being swivelled about its centre bolt by road irregularities.

THE COMMERCIAL VEHICLE

The arrangement and functions of the main components of the commercial vehicle are similar to those of the car but they are designed to carry much heavier loads, much more variety of load, and to operate at lower road speeds. All the larger commercial vehicles are now powered by diesel, or compression-ignition, engines which produce a high torque at comparatively low crankshaft speeds. The gearboxes may provide up to six different ratios, and may be secured to the engine or mounted as separate units. The final drive gear assembly may be of the spiral bevel; or hypoid, crown wheel and pinion type; or worm and wheel; or single- or two-speed, double-reduction types.

The commercial vehicle chassis, like that of the car, must be designed to suit the arrangement of the transmission, suspension, and steering systems, and these in turn will depend upon the loads to be carried and the position of the engine.

The various parts of the commercial chassis are forged from fairly thick steel plate and are all of much deeper section than those of the car chassis. The chassis assembly is much heavier and more rigid (see Fig. 1.6). Diagonal bracing is not often used but the cross-members are hot riveted to the deep-section side frames and wide gusset plates are used to add stiffness to the joints. Hot riveting is employed to obtain the maximum possible tightness of the joints. The side frames are not swept up at the front and rear to allow for the movement of the axles; usually the chassis is narrower at the forward end but it is not swept in to allow for the movement of the steering road wheels. This is because the engine is usually mounted higher in the chassis than a car engine, and because the turning circle is larger.

Damaged side frames must be removed for straightening and, if the bending involves less than 10°, heat should not be used. Hot riveting is essential during rebuilding. Emergency repairs only may be carried out on a joint, or spring mounting, by reaming out the existing rivet holes to the next size and fitting high-tensile steel bolts and lock washers.

With the exception of the smaller and lighter types of commercial vehicle, a beam axle and two longitudinally arranged leaf springs are fitted at the forward end of the chassis. Two longitudinal leaf springs are employed at the rear end and are secured to, and locate, a heavy tubular rear axle which supports the final drive gear assembly. This is driven by a propeller shaft which may be made in two parts, a centre bearing being fitted to a chassis cross-member about half-way along its length.

Attachment of components
The engine and the gearbox are supported in the chassis on mountings

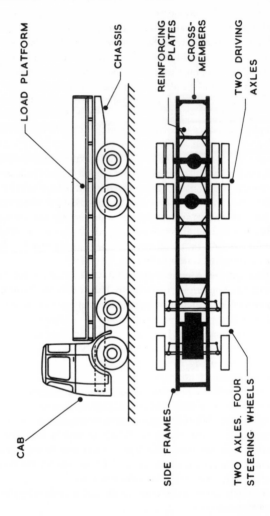

Fig. 1.6   Rigid chassis

of a special form of rubber. These mountings must not only support and locate their units but must also absorb vibration and, more important, resist the torque reaction forces. These forces try to make the unit rotate bodily when it is transmitting torque; i.e. when it is working against a load or resistance. (This tendency to rotate can be seen when an engine is accelerated while the vehicle is stationary.) In some engine installations these forces are limited by steady bars fitted between the engine and the chassis.

The leaf springs are attached to the chassis by shackle pins, a swing shackle being fitted at the rear end of each spring. The spring eyes are fitted with phosphor-bronze bushes and the shackle pins are drilled and fitted with grease nipples. The pins are passed through the spring eyes, and through steel forgings or castings called *hanger brackets*, and are secured by slotted nuts and split-pins. The hanger brackets are hot riveted to either the side or the underside of the chassis side frames.

The cab is an assembly of spot-welded, mild steel pressings and is bolted to the chassis. Rubber mountings and felt strips may be used to reduce vibration and noise. The body is built to suit the loads to be carried and to comply with legal requirements, and is attached to the chassis by locating and clamp bolts.

The steering gearbox is bolted and split-pinned directly to the chassis while the steering column is supported by brackets in the frame of the cab. Other components such as pedals and levers, power-servo units and fuel tanks, and special equipment such as hydraulic rams, are securely mounted on the chassis by riveting, bolting, or by bolted, rubber mounting plates.

Axles and road wheels

The larger and heavier commercial vehicles are usually fitted with three or four axles, and six or eight wheels. Some of these wheels may be of the twin-wheel type. Multi-axle designs are used because:

(1) The maximum weight on any one axle is limited by law. This is to protect the road surfaces from damage, and also to provide some measure of protection for the general public against the possible serious consequences of overloading vehicles.

(2) The maximum weight to be taken by an axle is limited by the load which a tyre can resist.

A twin wheel and tyre assembly can carry almost twice the weight of a single wheel and tyre but, because of the legal limit on the width of a vehicle, the chassis width must be reduced to make room for the extra tyre. This results in the need for the chassis to be made even more rigid. Apart from the legal limits of width, weight and length, and of the weight and type of load carried, commercial vehicles must be designed to operate within acceptable limits of cost – in terms of tonnes of load per kilometre.

Six- and eight-wheeled vehicles are produced with different axle arrangements and are classified according to their chassis design. Those in which the axles are all attached to one frame are known as *rigid* types. Those in which a tractor and trailer are intended to operate as a unit are called *articulated* types.

Rigid types, Fig. 1.6

Six-wheeled. These vehicles usually have two steering road wheels and either four driving road wheels or two driving wheels and two free-running wheels on a dead axle.

Eight-wheeled. The rear driving wheel arrangement is the same as that for six-wheeled types but four-wheel steering is fitted. The steering road wheels must be interlinked in such a way that true rolling motion of each wheel is obtained as the vehicle negotiates a corner.

Both of these types make use of the weight of the load to increase the adhesion or grip of the tyres of the driving wheels. These vehicles are about 48 m long and they therefore have a very large turning circle which makes them difficult to manœuvre in small spaces.

Articulated types, Fig. 1.7

In these types the engine and transmission are built into a short chassis which carries a very strong towing and swivelling attachment. This tractor assembly may have four or six wheels, two or four of which are driving wheels. The trailer which is coupled to the tractor may have two or four free-running wheels at the rear end.

Advantages over rigid types

(1) Articulated types are much more manœuvrable in a small space because of the smaller turning circle of the tractor, and because of the articulation itself.

(2) The trailer can be detached for loading and unloading – leaving the tractor free to carry on with other work.

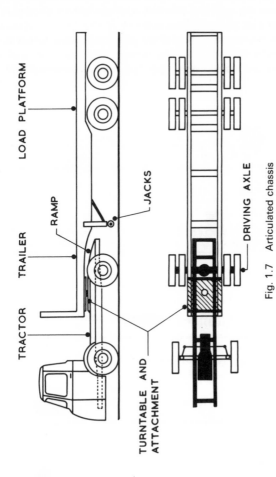

Fig. 1.7   Articulated chassis

Disadvantages

(1) The load is carried mainly by the dead axles so there is less adhesion between the tyres and the road. This may permit wheel spin and skidding under certain conditions.

(2) The arc of free movement of the coupling between the tractor and the trailer is limited, so making these vehicles unsuitable for use over uneven ground. On side slopes they can be very unstable.

CONVENTIONAL C.V.

FORWARD CONTROL C.V.

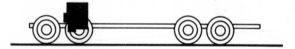

UNDERFLOOR P.S.V.

UNDERFLOOR REAR P.S.V.

TRANSVERSE REAR P.S.V.

Fig. 1.8   Engine positions: larger vehicles

Alternative arrangements of power and transmission units

Engine position. In the conventional commercial vehicle (c.v.) the engine is mounted in the forward end of the chassis, and must be fairly high off the ground to allow for the movement of the beam axle below the sump.

Extra load-carrying capacity can be provided in some forms of commercial vehicle by mounting the engine below the level of the floor. The engines used in this arrangement are called 'flat' engines and are usually those having horizontally opposed cylinders. Other forms are basically multi-cylinder in-line engines which have been redesigned to operate in the horizontal instead of the vertical plane.

Although flat engines are more commonly used in commercial vehicles, the advantage of space saving applies equally well to cars. The Hillman Imp and the Volkswagen Estate cars are examples of such use.

Some manufacturers of passenger service vehicles (p.s.v.) have been able to provide more capacity by employing the rear-engine rear-drive arrangement, so adding a further advantage to those of the arrangement generally. Examples of these are the Leyland Atlantean and the Daimler Fleetline.

Twin-axle drives. When heavy commercial vehicles are fitted with two driving axles, several alternative transmission arrangements are possible. The most common arrangement is that in which two final drive gear assemblies of the worm and wheel type are used; they are mounted one behind the other in the centres of the axles. The forward

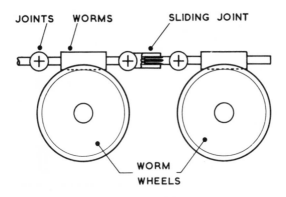

Fig. 1.9   Twin-axle drives

worm is driven by the propeller shaft from the rear of the gearbox. This worm drives its own wheel and differential, and at the same time drives the second worm through a short shaft. The shaft is fitted with two universal joints with a sliding joint arranged between them.

When the worm is arranged above the wheel a larger ground clearance is obtained. When the worm is below the wheel a lower platform is made possible. The later arrangement is used for buses and coaches.

In another arrangement of four-wheeled drive a single axle may be employed. This has the final drive gearing in its centre and each half-shaft drives a train of gears connected to two very short axles at each side of the vehicle. The gears and wheel axles are supported in a lever case which is pivoted upon the end of the axle at each side.

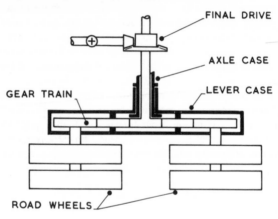

Fig. 1.10   Single-axle twin drive

THE MOTOR-CYCLE

The motor-cycle, being one of the earliest road vehicles, has been developed in many countries into a very reliable and efficient means of transport. Not only has it the advantages of being light in weight and economical to operate, but it can also be used over very rough country, under conditions where many four-wheeled vehicles would be brought to a standstill. Its users are seldom held up by traffic congestion but the one disadvantage is that riders do require protective clothing and equipment.

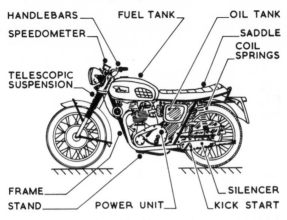

HANDLEBARS
SPEEDOMETER
FUEL TANK
OIL TANK
SADDLE
COIL SPRINGS
TELESCOPIC SUSPENSION
FRAME
STAND
POWER UNIT
SILENCER
KICK START

Fig. 1.11   Motor-cycle

Although many varieties of motor-cycle exist their construction generally consists of a rigid, brazed, tubular steel frame, which either incorporates or cradles the power unit. The latter is suitable both for the two- and the four-stroke cycle and may carry up to four air-cooled cylinders, each having its own carburettor. Kick-start devices are used instead of starter motors and twin silencer systems are almost universal. Coil ignition is general and multi-coil systems fairly common. The petrol tank is arranged above the engine and is fitted with knee grips. The oil tank is below the saddle, which is positioned above the rear mudguard extending from the back of the petrol tank. Foot rests protrude from low down in the frame and the chain-driven rear wheel is cushioned by large coil springs. The front wheel is turned by the handlebars, the swivelling being controlled by an adjustable damper and the wheel being carried between two telescopic hydraulic suspension tubes.

The electrical system includes a 12 V battery and many machines have a.c./d.c. alternators. A speedometer is fitted, together with an oil warning lamp and an ignition warning lamp.

The Body and Chassis

Separate chassis–body types

In this form of construction, now confined to the larger and heavier vehicles, the chassis and the body are each made as a separate unit and then bolted together. Although the body adds to the weight of the completed assembly it adds very little to its strength.

The shape of the chassis is determined by the location of the power unit, the arrangement of the suspension system and the loads to be carried. The function of the chassis is to act as the frame or skeleton of the vehicle, providing a mounting for all the other assemblies and keeping them in their correct relative positions, in spite of all the varying loads to which they are subjected. It must be strong and rigid, and is usually made from steel pressings which are welded and riveted together. Reinforcement is provided, where necessary, to add to its rigidity.

Essentially the chassis consists of two long side-members with shorter cross-members. The assembled shape varies between the different types of vehicle, those for commercial vehicles being simpler but much stronger and heavier. The side members are usually of channel section in commercial vehicles and of box section in cars, the latter being deeper in section between the wheels to provide greater resistance to bending load. The forward and rear ends are upswept to allow for the movement of the axles, and (in plan view) are made narrow at the forward end to allow a greater steering lock and therefore a smaller vehicle turning circle.

The cross-members connect the side members and are of channel, box or tubular section. They are welded, riveted or bolted to the side members. Additional cross-members are sometimes added to provide extra resistance to engine torque.

When independent types of suspension are used the chassis has to be made much more rigid to resist the twisting of the chassis members. The upsweep at the forward end is reduced and the engine is arranged

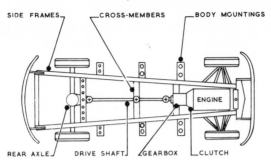

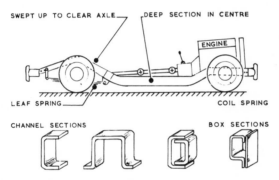

Fig. 2.1   Separate chassis

lower in the chassis. This improves the road-holding of the vehicle and is only possible because allowance for axle movement is now no longer required (no beam axle).

Chassis-floor

Many of the older cars and light commercial vehicles had plywood floors which added no strength or rigidity to the chassis–body assembly. Later types had a fluted, mild steel sheet floor which was welded to the chassis members. The combination of fluting and welding added greatly to the rigidity and, therefore, lighter gauges of sheet metal could be used for the whole assembly to reduce its weight, without sacrificing its strength.

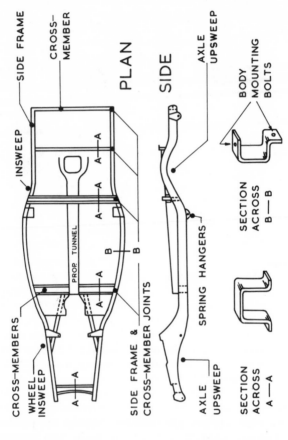

SIDE FRAME

CROSS-
MEMBER

PLAN

SIDE

AXLE
UPSWEEP

BODY
MOUNTING
BOLTS

INSWEEP

A—A

A—A

SECTION
ACROSS
B—B

PROP. TUNNEL

B——B

A—A

SIDE FRAME &
CROSS-MEMBER JOINTS

SPRING HANGERS

CROSS-MEMBERS

WHEEL
INSWEEP

A—A

A—A

AXLE
UPSWEEP

SECTION
ACROSS
A—A

Fig. 2.2   Chassis-floor

Body

With both of these main chassis types the body is made from a large number of steel pressings which are welded together. The body is bolted to the chassis at numerous points, rubber or felt strips being interposed to damp down vibration and noise.

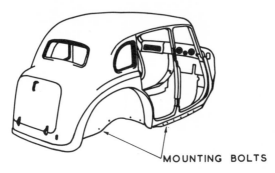

MOUNTING BOLTS

Fig. 2.3   Body only

Integral type

This is the modern form of construction for almost all cars and lighter commercial vehicles. It is light in weight and, when produced in very large numbers, is relatively cheap. The chassis, floor and body are assembled by welding from a very large number of mild steel pressings, each being correctly aligned by using jigs. Although particularly light the assembly is very strong because all the loads acting on it are spread over the whole of it. The chassis becomes a sub-frame in this form of construction and other sub-frames are often used for the front and rear suspension units, and sometimes for the final drive assembly. These detachable sub-frames are usually attached by rubber mountings to reduce the amount of noise and vibration transmitted to the body shell.

These body assemblies must be well protected from corrosion because of the thin steel employed. Chemical compounds and special paints have to be applied to the underside of the vehicle at regular intervals, and all boxed sections should be sprayed internally with anti-corrosion solutions. Water drain holes in these sections, and in doors must be kept clear. The vibration or 'drumming' of the larger panels is a

REAR

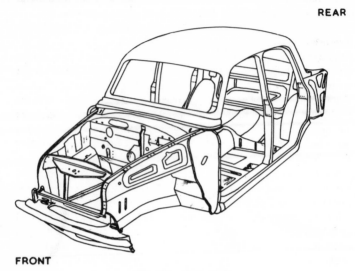

FRONT

Fig. 2.4   Body shell

common fault and special compounds are painted on their inner sides to reduce this. Felt may also be used.

Jacking points

In these assemblies certain points are reinforced to provide adequate resistance against the forces needed to lift the vehicle when wheels have to be removed. These points may be at the ends of the longitudinal sub-frames, or at one or two points in the sills at each side of the vehicle. The jacks to be used usually form a part of the equipment of the vehicle and are designed for use only with that vehicle. Generally they are screw-type jacks with a special side bar to fit into the body housing shaped to fit around it. Some types have a shaped hook instead of a bar. It is most important that the vehicle be on level, hard ground and that the other wheels be properly chocked to prevent the movement of the vehicle when the jack is in use. While these jacking systems are moderately successful they cannot be used safely except under ideal conditions.

The slightest movement of the vehicle will usually result in either the jack screw bending or the reinforcing giving way – either resulting in damage or injury, especially if the body is affected by corrosion.

Seat belts

Although modern body designs provide much more protection for the drivers and passengers in motor vehicles than was possible with the separate chassis–body types, the ever-increasing speeds result in more serious injuries when collisions do occur. There is no doubt that the correct use of seat belts can do a very great deal to reduce the severity of the injuries received. Many drivers have had only minor injuries when the vehicle has been a complete 'write-off' – even at speeds of over 90 km/hour.

Seat belts are used to prevent the body being hurled forward when the vehicle is stopped suddenly. The force involved may be as high as 10 000 N at high-speed impact so the security of the attachment of the belt to the vehicle is of the utmost importance. Most belts are secured by bolts which are screwed into threaded anchor plates welded into the centre door pillars and the inner faces of the sills or floor. These must be checked for corrosion damage, and to ensure they are still secure, at intervals during the life of the vehicle and the necessary repairs made at once.

Where belts have to be fitted and anchorages are not provided it is most important that the locations selected are correct. These vary with belt types but usually involve the fitting of three anchorages such that the belts hold the body to the seat and the shoulders to the seat back. Extra reinforcing plates, of generous area, should be welded in and bolts of about 16 mm diameter be used with large plain washers. In some types U-bolts are provided and extra-thickness reinforcement is required. The more expensive belts are of the inertia reel type. These permit the gentle movement of the body but lock automatically when a sudden and violent movement is made. The less expensive types are less convenient because they hold all the time. All types have a quick release fastener, and all belts fitted should be checked as being of the approved British Standard material strength.

Seat location

For reasons of safety and comfort all driving or front seats must be adjustable in relation to the controls. This is usually obtained by mounting the seat on some form of sliding runners with spring-loaded location locks. These may be pins fitting into holes or spring pawls, a lever withdrawing them when adjustment is needed. Some modern seats will also permit the adjustment of the seat angle in both the horizontal and vertical planes, and a very few will allow the seat to swivel. It is very important that these devices are maintained in good order and that no movement of the seat occurs during the movement of the vehicle. A seat must never be allowed to tilt or, particularly, slide backwards – the driver will lose control at once if this should occur.

The Suspension and Steering Systems

The front axle

Beam axle

This is a high-grade alloy steel forging which is heat treated to provide

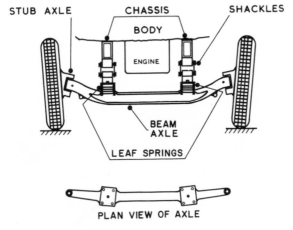

Fig. 3.1   Front axle arrangement

the maximum possible degree of toughness. Between the spring bed-plates it is usually of I-shaped cross-section to enable it to resist bending loads. The bed-plates are flat platforms forged from the beam and are used to both locate and mount the axle to the springs. The ends of the beam are upswept and of oval section to resist the action of the braking torque which tries to turn the axle with the road wheel. A forged alloy steel stub axle is secured to each end of the beam by means of a 'king pin' or 'swivel' pin, the pins and axles being arranged at the correct angles for the steering geometry. Details of the stub axle are shown in Fig. 3.2.

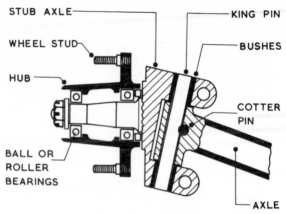

Fig. 3.2   Stub axle detail

Leaf springs

Leaf springs are usually semi-elliptical in shape and are built up from separate lengths of a fatigue-resisting alloy steel, each leaf being hardened and tempered. The main leaf has eyes formed at each end into which are fitted phosphor-bronze or special rubber bushes; see Fig. 3.3 for arrangement. Shackle pins are passed through these bushes and the chassis brackets to secure the spring to the chassis. Each end of the second leaf is wrapped part of the way around each eye to provide extra support to the main leaf when the spring is deflected. The remaining leaves are progressively shorter to even out the stress along the length of the spring. The leaves are fastened together by a centre bolt. The head of the centre bolt is large and cylindrical and is used to locate the axle in relation to the chassis, the bolt head fitting into a hole in the axle bedplate.

Clips are fitted at points along the length of the spring to prevent the leaves moving out of alignment and fouling the chassis. They also prevent the main leaf being subjected to all of the load. Strips of rubber or a soft metal may be used between the leaves to reduce the friction between them (by natural damping).

Shackles. The springs are secured to the chassis by shackle pins. The front end of the spring is secured by passing a shackle pin through a U-shaped bracket riveted or welded to the chassis and through the

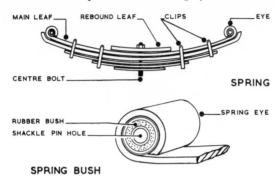

Fig. 3.3   Spring and spring bush

spring eye bush. The rear end of the spring is secured by two shackle-plates and pins and this is known as a *swinging shackle* (Fig. 3.4). Swinging shackles are used to allow the spring to extend as it is deflected. If the shackle pins are fitted into phosphor-bronze bushes, or into the plain eye, the pins are drilled for oil ways and fitted with grease nipples.

The axle is secured to the springs by means of U-shaped bolts or plain bolts of high-tensile steel.

Arrangement of springs and axle
Two leaf springs are arranged parallel to, and below, the forward end of each chassis side frame. The beam axle is prevented from moving forwards and backwards, and from side to side, by the action of the spring centre bolt heads locating in the axle.

Forces acting
When the vehicle is driven forward the axle is pulled along by the forward half of the spring so this portion is under a tensile load. The whole spring is subjected to a bending load due to the weight of the vehicle, and shock loads from the road wheels.

When the brakes are applied the axle tries to turn with the wheels and this is prevented by the spring, i.e. the spring acts as a torque arm bent down at the front and up at the rear. When one wheel only is deflected the whole spring is subjected to twist or torsion load. These forces are illustrated in Fig. 3.4.

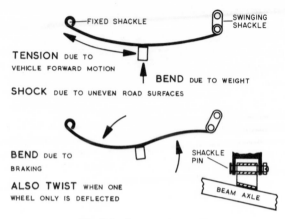

Fig. 3.4   Front spring loads

The rear axle

Axle case

Axles are classified as 'live' or 'dead' types. A dead axle is one which does not rotate, the wheel rotating upon the axle either directly or upon bearings mounted on the axle; as with stub axles and caravan axles. A

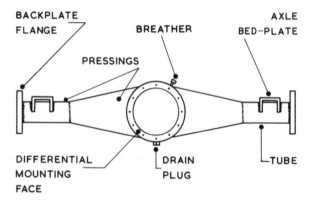

Fig. 3.5   Banjo axle case

live axle is one which rotates with the wheel and is supported in ball or roller bearings mounted on or inside an axle case.

The axle case acts as a beam to support the weight of the chassis and body (taken on the bed-plate) and provides a mounting for the final drive mechanism. It also acts as an oil tank for the lubrication of the final drive. The 'banjo' construction (see Fig. 3.5) is often used for the rear axle cases of the smaller and lighter vehicles. In these two steel pressings are riveted or welded together and reinforced as required to carry the final drive mechanism, the axle or half-shaft bearings, and for securing the axle case to the springs.

In rear axle designs the axle is made in two halves. The inner end of each half-shaft is supported in the sun wheels of the differential assembly while their outer ends are carried in a bearing at the outer ends of the axle case.

REAR SUSPENSION (CARS)

The design of both the chassis and the suspension system at the rear end depends upon the arrangement of the transmission system. In cars and light commercial vehicles two main types of system have been used. These are the open, or Hotchkiss, drive (which is the type most often employed) and the enclosed, or torque tube, drive. In both of these the final drive gear assembly is mounted in the rear axle case and therefore rises and falls as the springs are deflected.

The open shaft (Hotchkiss) drive
Suspension
In this design a semi-elliptical leaf spring is fitted under each chassis side frame at the rear end. The forward end of each spring is shackled directly to the chassis while the rear end is secured by means of a swinging shackle. Rubber type bushes are usually fitted into the spring eyes and hanger brackets. The axle may be mounted above or below the springs, and it is prevented from moving sideways and from front to rear by the enlarged heads of the spring centre bolts. These are fitted into recesses in the axle bed-plates. The axle is secured to the springs by high-tensile steel U-bolts or clamp bolts and plates. In most modern designs rubber pads are fitted between the springs and the axle to reduce the noise and vibration transmitted from the axle into the chassis and body.

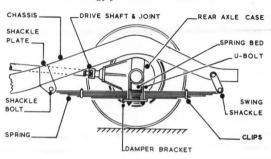

Fig. 3.6   Hotchkiss drive

Forces acting

In all rear suspension designs the following forces are acting on the axle, and these forces must be controlled or limited in their action by the arrangement of the suspension.

(1) *Driving thrust.* When driving torque is applied to the road wheels it acts at the point of contact between the tyre and the road to produce the driving thrust or tractive effort. The axle is moved forward and this movement, or thrust force, must be transferred to the chassis.

(2) *Braking thrust.* When the brakes are applied the movement of the rear axle is retarded. This action must also be transferred to the chassis.

The driving and braking thrusts act through the same components but in opposite directions to each other.

(3) *Torque reaction.* When driving torque is applied to the road wheels they resist the torque. This produces an opposing, or reaction, force of equal size on the axle case. This forces the pinion nose upward (i.e. twists the axle) and this movement must be limited either by the springs of the suspension system or by means of radius rods or torque arms.

(4) *Brake reaction.* When the brakes are applied the wheel is retarded and the reaction force, acting through the brake back-plate, twists the axle and forces the pinion nose to move down. This twisting of the axle must also be limited.

The torque and braking reaction forces act through the same components but in opposite directions.

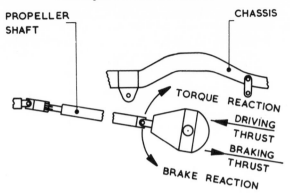

Fig. 3.7   Forces acting

Transmission

The gearbox output shaft is connected to the differential pinion by a hollow and fairly large diameter drive or propeller shaft. These two shafts are at different heights and two universal joints are required, one at each end of the shaft. This is partly because of the difference in heights and partly because the pinion nose, under the influence of the driving and braking torques, describes an arc having the axle as its centre. As the wheels are deflected by road irregularities the rear axle swings in an arc which has the fixed spring shackle as its centre. This increases the distance between the pinion and the gearbox output shaft and is allowed for by fitting a sliding joint at the forward end of the propeller shaft (see Fig. 7.14).

Effects of forces

(1) The driving thrust is transferred from the axle to the chassis by the forward ends of the springs, acting through the fixed shackles. (Front half of each spring is subjected to compressive stress.)

(2) The braking thrust is transferred to the chassis in the same manner but in the opposite direction. (Front half of each spring is subjected to tensile stress.)

(3) The driving torque reaction force, which tries to twist the axle in the opposite direction to that of the road wheel, is prevented from completely turning the axle by the action of the springs. Each spring

acts as a torque arm and is (to a varying extent) deformed by the force, being twisted *up at the front* and *down at the rear*.

(4) The braking torque reaction forces also twist the axle and are restrained by the springs acting as torque arms. As they resist, the springs are again deformed, being twisted *down at the front* and *up at the rear*.

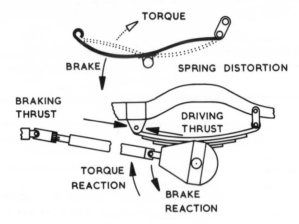

Fig. 3.8   Effects of forces

In this arrangement of the transmission and suspension systems the springs are subjected to the following loads:

(a) Bending loads due to the weight of the vehicle.

(b) Tensile loads due to the braking thrust.

(c) Compressive loads due to the driving thrust.

(d) Torsion or twisting loads when only one spring is deflected.

(e) Bending loads due to the driving and braking torque reaction forces.

These springs must, therefore, be very strong and relatively heavy.

The torque tube drive (enclosed)

Suspension

A single semi-elliptical leaf spring is fitted across the chassis, being located in a chassis cross-member by its centre bolt and secured by high-tensile steel U-bolts. As the spring is fitted both transversely and inverted, the axle ends are secured to the spring ends. Two swinging

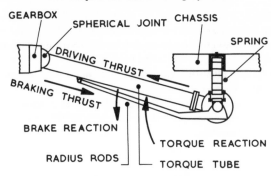

Fig. 3.9   Torque tube drive

shackles are fitted, and special rubber bushes are bonded to the shackle pins so that the movement of the shackles is limited. The ends of the axle and spring are prevented from moving forward and backward by a vee-shaped radius rod which also prevents the ends of the spring and axle from turning about the spring centre.

The lower end of the propeller shaft is secured to the pinion shaft by a splined sleeve which is riveted to each shaft. The upper end of the propeller shaft is fitted into a sliding joint attached to a universal joint arranged so that the centre of the joint coincides with the centre of the cupped end of the tubular torque member.

As the axle and spring are deflected by the road wheels, they and the torque tube swing in an arc having as its centre the centre of the single universal joint. A second joint is not required as the end of the pinion shaft is always in exact alignment with the end of the propeller shaft. The radius rod is connected between the ends of the axle and a point along the length of the tubular torque member.

REAR SUSPENSION (COMMERCIAL VEHICLES)

Single axle

The rear suspension for a commercial vehicle with a single rear axle is similar to that of the conventional car, employing an open propeller shaft and two leaf springs. Where the chassis is a long wheelbase type the propeller shaft is made in two parts with a thrust bearing near the centre of the shaft length.

Twin axles

The twin-axle arrangement as used in six- and eight-wheeled vehicles is designed as a single unit known as a *bogie*. The main requirements of the bogie are:

(1) That, under all normal operating conditions, the loads imposed on each axle be maintained equally.

(2) That the axles be kept as close to each other as possible. This is to reduce the tendency of the rear road wheels to slide or skid when the vehicle is cornering.

Load equalisation. This is also called compensation, and is obtained by some system of levers which are attached to the springs in such a way that any extra load imposed on one axle is partly transferred to the other. The driving and braking torques, and their reaction forces, are transferred to the chassis and controlled in a similar manner to that of the single-axle design.

Skid tendency, Fig. 3.10. When the vehicle is cornering, the centre of

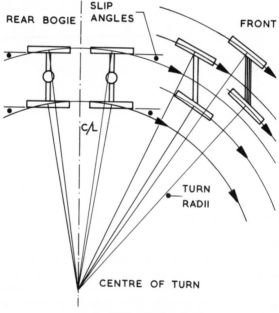

Fig. 3.10   Skid tendency

its turn will lie on a line parallel with the axles and midway between them. As the rear wheels cannot take up a position at right angles to their radii of turn they cannot rotate under a true rolling motion. They are therefore partly dragged or skidded round. The amount of skidding is reduced by arranging the axles as closely as possible. In practice, the effect of this skid tendency on the handling of the vehicle is not serious because this type of vehicle is normally operated at low speeds and under heavy loads.

Types of bogie

Balance beam, Fig. 3.11. In this arrangement the springs are mounted on the outer sides of the chassis side frames. The front end of the forward spring and the rear end of the rear spring are shackled directly to the chassis. A balance beam is secured to the chassis midway between the two axles. This beam pivots about its centre and its ends are connected

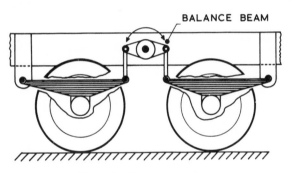

BALANCE BEAM

Fig. 3.11   Balance beam bogie

to the rear of the forward spring and the front end of the rear spring. As one axle is lifted, the beam is tilted to force the other axle down to take its share of the extra load. Vehicles fitted with this type of suspension bogie must be limited to use on roads. This is because the spring deflection is limited by the length of the balance beam, which must be kept short so keeping the axles close together and reducing the skid tendency.

Trunnion, Fig. 3.12. In this arrangement each chassis side frame supports a trunnion block to which the spring centres are secured. The springs are inverted and pivoting axle clamps are fitted between the ends of the springs. When one wheel is deflected the whole assembly pivots on the trunnion shaft and so forces the other axle and wheel down to take its share of the extra load.

The trunnion bogie is usually used where the nature of the load or the type of body will permit the use of a narrow chassis. Twin wheels are usually fitted.

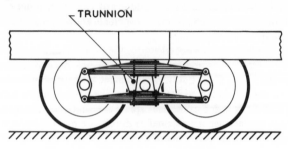

Fig. 3.12   Trunnion bogie

Bell crank, Fig. 3.13. In this arrangement the axles are brought close together and steering is easier. The skid tendency is much reduced but the whole arrangement is much more complicated and heavier, and it requires much more attention in service.

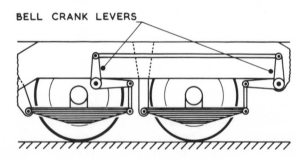

Fig. 3.13   Bell crank bogie

INDEPENDENT SUSPENSION

The beam axle and leaf spring suspension arrangements have the disadvantage that when one wheel is deflected its movement is transmitted by the axle to the other wheel and the body of the vehicle – affecting both the steering and the comfort of the ride. Leaf springs are also heavy and limit the deflection of the wheel. When they are used at the front they also necessitate mounting the engine fairly high in the chassis. These factors reduce the safety and ease of handling of the vehicle and therefore suspension arrangements are used in which wheels may be independently sprung.

Cars may be sprung independently at the front only, or at both front and rear – the steering and braking systems being designed to suit the suspension. The chassis or sub-frame must be made stronger and more rigid but the engine can be mounted much nearer to the ground. The springs, whether coil, torsion bar or rubber, can be set farther apart. These factors increase the road-holding and safe handling qualities as well as driver and passenger comfort. The forces acting on the suspension units are the same as those described for the leaf springs but they are limited and transmitted in different ways in the different arrangements.

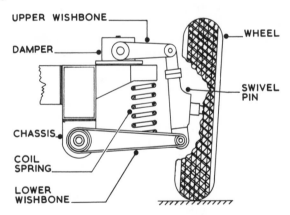

Fig. 3.14   Coil spring front suspension

One of the most commonly used arrangements incorporates a large coil spring and two wishbone-shaped arms. The larger wishbone is secured to the chassis or sub-frame at its wider end by rubber bushes. The outer or narrow end is secured to a swivel pin assembly which carries the stub axle. The upper end of the swivel pin is secured to the outer end of a smaller wishbone arm fitted above the larger arm. The inner end of the upper arm is splined to the spindle of a damper unit bolted to the sub-frame. The large coil spring is fitted between the lower wishbone and an inverted cup projecting from the sub-frame. The cup and the wishbone are shaped to locate the ends of the spring. One such assembly is arranged at each side of the vehicle.

When a wheel is deflected by a road surface irregularity the lower wishbone is forced upward and the spring is compressed. The spring then rebounds to force the wheel back on to the road, the damper absorbing the energy given out by the spring. The other wheel and the rest of the vehicle are only very slightly affected.

Where coil springs are used for the rear suspension, special provision must be made to locate the axle relative to the sub-frame (driving and braking thrust forces) and to control the driving and braking torques. This is usually carried out by fitting radius arms between the ends of the axle and the sub-frame such that the axle case cannot be turned by the torques.

Dampers

When a leaf or a coil spring receives a hard blow it is deflected and then rebounds until it has dissipated all the energy it has received. Because this causes a very uncomfortable ride and may well make the vehicle

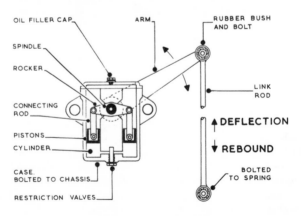

Fig. 3.15   Piston damper

uncontrollable, hydraulic dampers are used to absorb the energy as quickly as possible.

Modern dampers operate on both spring deflection and rebound, a special oil or fluid being forced through restriction valves from one cylinder to another. The pistons of the cylinders are linked to the suspension and the resistance to the movement of the suspension is automatically varied to suit the severity of the shock load on the spring. The energy given out by the spring is converted into heat and this is dissipated by the stream of air passing under the vehicle.

Piston dampers are fitted where spring deflection is small. Tubular dampers are used with large-deflection spring arrangements which provide a softer ride. Tubular dampers may also be used to reduce roll, being inclined as shown. Roll may also be reduced by stabilisers, or anti-roll bars, which are used to link the lower wishbone arms (or damper arms) across the vehicle. These arms offer resistance to their being twisted as the vehicle rolls and so help to keep the vehicle vertical when cornering.

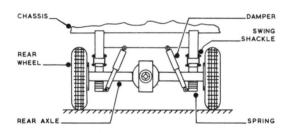

Fig. 3.16   Telescopic damper layout

WHEELS AND TYRES

Wheels

Vehicle wheels consist of a pressed-steel disc to which a pressed-steel rim is riveted or welded. A rubber tyre containing air is mounted upon the rim to increase the grip of the wheel upon the road and to reduce the transmission of shock and vibration from the uneven road surface to the body of the vehicle.

The centre disc of the wheel is dished and has a radially arranged set of conically reinforced holes. These holes pass over the securing studs of the hub mounted upon the axle or axle case. The wheel nuts have conical ends which engage with the conical holes to both centralise and secure the wheel to the hub. The disc is also either slotted or pierced with holes to allow a stream of air to pass through the wheel to help cool the brake drum.

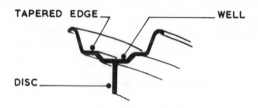

Fig. 3.17   Well base

In car wheels the centre portion of the rim is formed into a well into which the inextensible beads of the tyre must be forced when it is being fitted or removed. These wheels are known as well-base types, the beads being forced by the pressure of the air to lock upon the tapered edges of the rim and not upon the flanges.

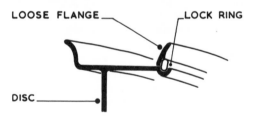

Fig. 3.18   Detachable flange

Commercial vehicle tyres have to be much larger and stronger, to carry the heavier loads, and therefore cannot be forced into a well when being assembled to a wheel. The rims used for these heavier tyres are of the detachable-flange, or the split-rim, type in which the tyre is slid over part of the rim before the rim is assembled. The centre disc of the wheel must also be larger and stronger, and it is dished to a much greater extent. Twin-wheel assemblies are also often used.

In the detachable-flange types the loose flange is retained by a very strong, split, steel ring which snaps into a recess in the centre disc. The rim is flat except for a slight taper near the integral flange which locks the bead as the tyre is inflated to its correct pressure.

A lighter type of detachable flange is combined with the lock ring and the rim has a shallow well to assist in fitting. In these types a bead lock taper is also used.

DISC RIMS BOLTED TOGETHER

Fig. 3.19   Split rim

Some vehicles are fitted with a split-rim type of wheel in which each rim half is integral with a centre disc, the two halves being bolted together by a ring of bolts and nuts. These are often painted red and are the outer ring of nuts. It is most important that they are never undone by mistake for the wheel securing nuts!

Note. All of these commercial vehicle wheel and tyre assemblies must always be placed behind a strong steel frame when the tyre is to be inflated – many mechanics have been killed or severely injured by lock rings which have blown off as a result of careless fitting.

Securing nuts of all types must be tightened down in the correct diagonal sequence and to the correct torque loading.

Tyres

Tyres are made from soft rubber reinforced by layers or plies of rayon or nylon cord. A harder rubber is used for the tread. The cords or plies may be arranged on the radii of the wheel produced (radial ply) or in such a way that they cross each other at an angle to the radii (cross ply). The numbers of plies used, and their arrangement, determine the properties or characteristics of the tyre e.g. radial-ply tyres operate at lower temperatures than cross-ply tyres and hold the road better – but they give a harder ride at low road speeds.

Mixing

It is because of these different properties that great care must always be taken in the way different types of tyre are arranged on the vehicle. A wrong arrangement makes the vehicle behave differently at different speeds and is therefore liable to cause an accident. Tyres of the same type and tread should always be fitted to any one axle. Manufacturers' advice on mixing must be adhered to but generally cross-ply types can be fitted at the front with radial-ply at the rear. The reverse must never be allowed as a dangerous degree of 'oversteer' will result.

Tubes

Most commercial vehicle tyres are used in conjunction with an inner tube which has an inflator valve secured to it. The valve passes through the rim and the tube is protected from the rim by a rubber liner strip. As the tube is inflated to the correct pressure (behind the guard) it supports the walls of the tyre and forces the beads up the rim tapers to lock the tyre to the rim. Punctures may be repaired by hot or cold vulcanised patches.

Tubeless

Most car tyres are of the tubeless type in which the tyre has an extra lining of soft rubber. This seals the tyre to the rim at each bead. The valve is arranged in a rubber body and is also sealed to the rim, the rim itself being airtight. The bead lock tapers are steeper in rims designed for tubeless tyres and these tyres must therefore not be fitted to tubed type rims.

Note

(1) Plugging a tubeless tyre to repair a puncture must only be considered as a temporary repair. Your customer must be warned that vulcanising is essential to complete the repair before he attempts any high-speed driving otherwise a 'blow-out' may occur.

(2) Minimum legal requirements now apply to tyres. Very briefly these are that:

   (a) Tyres must be suited to their use.

   (b) Tyres must be correctly inflated, have no cuts or bulges, and no plies must be exposed.

   (c) The tread pattern must not be re-cut, and there must be at least 1 mm depth of tread for at least three-quarters of the breadth of the tyre.

STEERING SYSTEMS

Function

The function of the steering system is to enable the driver to control accurately the direction taken by the vehicle under all operating conditions. The system must be light and easy to operate, free from shock and vibration, and be as direct as possible.

Arrangement

Each front road wheel rotates upon a stub axle. The stub axle pivots on a swivel pin or 'king pin' mounted at the correct angle in the end of a beam axle. (Details are shown in Fig. 3.2.) A track arm is attached to each stub axle and the two arms are linked by a track rod (Fig. 3.20). The connections are made by ball or rubber joints which allow for wheel movement but permit no slackness in the connection. The off-side track arm is extended and connected to the end of the steering gearbox drop arm by a drag link, ball or rubber joints again being used.

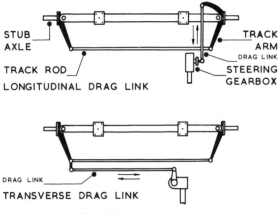

Fig. 3.20   Steering linkages

The steering gearbox is mounted on the chassis at the correct angle for the steering wheel and operates in such a way that the rotation of the steering wheel produces a forward and backward, or transverse, motion of the drop arm and drag link. This motion is transferred to the track rod and stub axles and results in the steering road wheels being swivelled about their king pins.

True rolling motion

As motor vehicles are steered by the side swivelling of the front wheels it is very important, to reduce tyre and bearing wear, that the wheels rotate on their axles with a true rolling motion, i.e. free from tyre 'scrub' when the vehicle is negotiating a turn. True rolling motion at each wheel

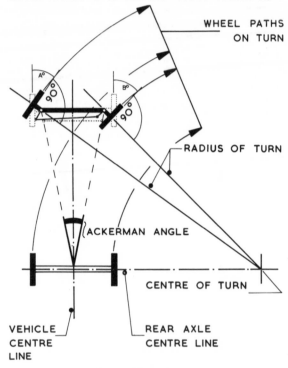

Fig. 3.21 Ackerman steering. Dotted lines indicate the straight-ahead positions of the wheels, track arms and track rod

is only obtained when each wheel is at 90° to a line drawn between the king pin and the centre of the turn. The centre of the turn always lies on the centre line of the rear axle and the rear wheels will always roll true because they are fixed at 90° to the rear axle.

The front wheels must follow a path which is an arc centred on the centre of turn. The front wheels must follow arcs of different length and radius, the outer wheel being the larger radius. So that both of them align themselves at 90° to their own radius of turn, they must be turned at different angles from the straight ahead position. This automatically-correct alignment is obtained by the use of the 'Ackerman' steering angle and principle (see Fig. 3.21).

The track rod is shorter than the distance between the king pins, and the ends of the track rod lie on a line projected at each side of the vehicle from the king pin to a point on the vehicle centre line on or near the pinion nose of the rear axle. In the straight ahead position the track rod lies parallel to the axle but, as it moves the track arms, the inner end moves nearer to the axle than the outer end. This results in the inner track arm and wheel being turned through a larger angle than the outer wheel. The difference between these angles is not constant but is automatically correct to maintain the wheels at 90° to any radius of turn.

Four-wheeled steering, Fig. 3.22

The arrangement of the steering linkages is almost that of two-wheeled steering duplicated but the drag link consists of two parts. Both are

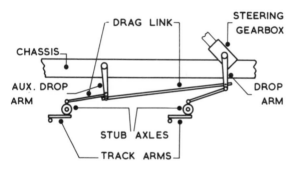

Fig. 3.22   Four-wheeled steering linkage

connected to an auxiliary drop arm, or compensating lever, by ball joints but in different positions. The rear-axle drag link is connected to the higher ball joint, so being given less movement than that of the forward-axle drag link. The rear steering road wheels therefore turn through a smaller number of degrees than those of the forward wheels.

By careful proportioning of the linkages the Ackerman angle is maintained and the wheels maintain a true rolling motion as the vehicle takes a corner.

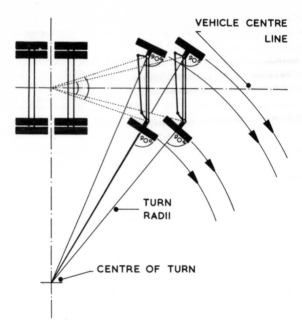

Fig. 3.23   Four-wheeled steering geometry

Steering gearboxes

Types

All steering mechanisms employ some form of gearing which makes possible the changes in force direction and size needed to swivel the road wheels about their king pins. The worm is the basic component of a large number of different types of steering gearbox and it is used in conjunction with any of the following: (a) a wheel, (b) a sector of a wheel, (c) a nut, (d) a roller, and (e) a system of recirculating steel balls. There are also the cam and peg, and the rack and pinion designs.

Variations of these basic designs are also used in which the mechanical efficiency is increased, and friction reduced to a minimum, by the use of balls or rollers.

Reduction

All steering gearboxes employ reduction gears in which a large steering wheel movement under a small torque is converted into a smaller drag link movement under a much larger torque. The usual reduction is about 14:1 but, as the drop arm needs only a small arc of motion, 3 or 4 complete revolutions of the steering wheel will turn the road wheels fully from one side to the other, i.e. from lock to lock. Commercial vehicles, with their much bigger tyres and heavier wheel loadings, may require 8 to 10 turns of the steering wheel to move the road wheels from one lock to the other.

Steering lock

This is related to the smallest radius of turn which the vehicle can make to either the left or right. A 'good' or large lock resulting in a small radius of turn, is essential for easy manœuvring, and large locks are always provided for taxis and small delivery vehicles. These can usually turn inside a circle of about 7 m in diameter. Small and family cars are usually able to turn in a 9 m diameter circle, while the larger cars and commercial vehicles may have turning circles of between 9 m and 15 m in diameter. The longer the vehicle the larger its turning circle.

Semi-reversible steering

As both the reversible and irreversible systems are not suitable for motor vehicle purposes, an intermediate system is used. This is the semi-reversible steering system in which, by careful design of the steering gearbox, the road wheels are allowed to turn the steering wheel to a slight extent while the shock loads and vibrations are not transmitted.

Note. The steering gearboxes described in this chapter are basic designs. Many different versions are in service in which the basic design has been adapted to make it suitable for use with the different forms of independent front suspension. The column and tube arrangement has also been modified in many cases, and some are designed to collapse in the event of a severe impact – so reducing the possible chances of the driver being fatally injured in a crash.

The worm and wheel, Fig. 3.24

In almost all steering gearbox assemblies the steering wheel is attached
to the upper end of a strong steel tube, or column, by means of splines
(or a taper and key) and is secured with a lock-nut. At the lower end of
the column a rigidly secured *worm* (a large screw thread) engages with a

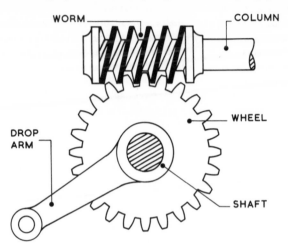

Fig. 3.24   Worm and wheel steering

worm-wheel, so that rotation of the worm causes the drop arm and shaft
to move in an arc of between 60° and 80°. The gearing is supported and
enclosed by a cast iron or aluminium alloy box which is filled with gear
oil and bolted to the chassis. The column is enclosed by a light steel
tube which is riveted to the box at its lower end while its upper end is
supported by a body bracket.

In the worm and wheel steering gearbox, a hardened steel worm is
engaged with a phosphor-bronze worm-wheel mounted upon a shaft to
which the drop arm is splined. Several complete revolutions of the worm
cause the wheel to move through an arc and so move the drop arm
through the same arc. The advantage of this type is that as only about
one-quarter of the wheel teeth are used in a lock-to-lock movement
wear is easily compensated for by repositioning the wheel on its shaft –
so bringing unworn teeth into mesh for another period of service. The

size of the worm-wheel and its cost are disadvantages which have led to this type being replaced by the worm and sector type.

Worm and sector, Fig. 3.25
This is similar in arrangement and operation to the worm and worm-wheel type, the sector being a part of a wheel. The sector is often mounted above the worm with the drag link end of the drop arm being below the worm. This type is smaller, cheaper and easier to install than the complete wheel type. Provision is made to compensate for the wear of the teeth and for the end-float adjustment of the worm and of the sector shaft.

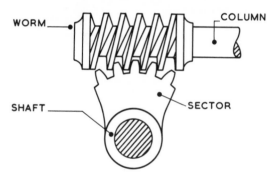

Fig. 3.25   Worm and sector steering

Worm and nut, Fig. 3.26
This type is used in many cars and commercial vehicles. The worm has more threads than those previously described and two-start threads may be used to obtain a greater axial movement. A fairly long, cylindrical nut of steel or phosphor-bronze is fitted upon the worm which, when rotated, moves the nut. This lateral motion is converted into a rotational motion of the cross-shaft and drop arm by means of a peg which is fitted into a bushed hole in the side of the nut. The nut is prevented from rotating with the worm by means of this peg or by having one flat side which slides along a flat face inside the box. The cross-shaft is supported by phosphor-bronze bushes and a spring-loaded oil seal is fitted at its outer end. Longitudinal movement of the worm and column is controlled by an adjustable ball bearing fitted at

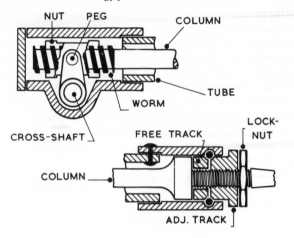

Fig. 3.26   Worm and nut steering

the steering wheel end of the column, and this is the only adjustment provided for. Wear between the worm and the nut, which results in excessive free play in the steering, must be corrected by replacing the column and worm and the nut.

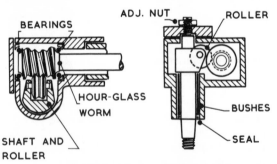

Fig. 3.27   Worm and roller steering

Worm and roller, Fig. 3.27
In these designs a single or double roller is mounted between two arms integral with the inner end of the cross-shaft, and this roller is meshed

with the worm. The roller is free to turn on its shaft and moves in an arc, the correct mesh being obtained throughout its movement by the hour-glass shape of the worm. The worm is supported and located by two ball or taper-roller bearings mounted in the case and its end-float may be adjusted by shims placed between the outer bearing track and the end-plate of the case. The roller shaft is eccentric and may be turned to compensate for wear between the roller and the worm. The upper end of the column is supported in the tube by a felt bush.

Recirculating ball, Fig. 3.28

This design resembles that of the worm and nut but the square threads are replaced by coarse pitch helical grooves of semi-circular cross-section. The outer ends of the groove in the nut are joined by a bolted-on steel tube which completes a path for the free-running steel balls with which the nut groove is filled. The cross-shaft carries a peg which is engaged with a hole in the side of the nut. As the worm is rotated, the nut is wound up or down the worm and the balls pass around their circuit. The only contact between the nut and the worm is made through the point contacts of the balls, and friction is therefore very

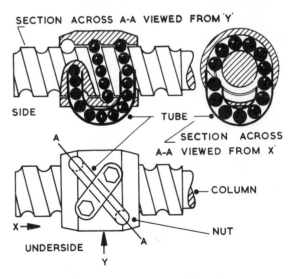

Fig. 3.28   Recirculating ball steering

low. The only adjustment possible is that of column end-float and this is controlled by an adjustable ball bearing fitted at the upper end of the column.

Worm and peg, Fig. 3.29

This may also be known as the cam and peg steering gearbox. The worm, or cam, resembles an Acme thread; i.e. it is a coarse pitch helical groove with flat sides and base, and is supported and located in ball

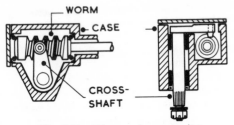

Fig. 3.29   Worm and peg steering

bearings mounted in the case. The end-float of the cam may be adjusted by shims fitted between the outer bearing and the end-plate. The inner end of the cross-shaft carries a tapered steel peg which is meshed with the cam. As the peg travels in an arc it is lifted by the cam, reaching its highest point in the forward position of the wheels. An adjusting screw and lock-nut or shims are fitted over the end of the cross-shaft to control its end-float at this point. The upper end of the column is supported in the tube by a felt bush.

Rack and pinion, Fig. 3.30

The rack consists of a cylindrical steel bar which has gear teeth machined on one side. The steel pinion is meshed with these teeth and is attached to the lower end of the column so that rotation of the steering wheel causes the rack to move bodily along its axis. In one modern arrangement the box, or case, is cylindrical and is mounted across the chassis. Each end of the rack is connected to the steering track arms by short, ball-joined shafts. Independent front suspension is fitted and torsion bars are used for springs. The lighter versions of this design make no provision for wear compensation, but the heavier versions have a shim adjustment which forces the pinion into closer contact with the rack.

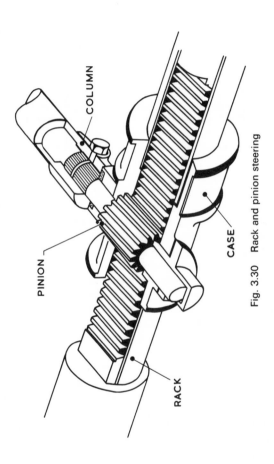

COLUMN

PINION

CASE

RACK

Fig. 3.30 Rack and pinion steering

4   The Spark-ignition Engine

Main components, Figs. 4.1–4.3

The petrol engine in a vehicle usually has four cylinders which are arranged in a straight line. Each cylinder is a hole bored in a cast iron block and each must be round, parallel, accurate in size and have a good surface finish. A cast iron cylinder head is bolted to the top of the cylinder block to seal off each of the bores, a gasket being fitted between them to make the joint pressure-tight (see Fig. 4.1). The petrol and air mixture is burned in the combustion chambers which are formed in the cylinder head above each cylinder.

The cylinder bores and combustion chambers are surrounded by hollow spaces filled with water. These spaces are called *water jackets* and they are used to carry away some of the excessive heat produced by the burning of the mixture. In this way the engine is protected from possible damage due to overheating.

Ports, or passages, are formed in the cylinder head or block to permit the entry and exit of the gases to and from the combustion chambers. The flow of these gases is controlled by the use of valves, each cylinder having one inlet and one exhaust valve.

Each cylinder contains a gas-tight plug or *piston* (see Fig. 4.2). Pistons are made from an aluminium alloy which is light in weight, has good heat-conducting qualities, and is fairly hard wearing. Because the aluminium alloy expands more than the cast iron of the cylinder block, when both are heated, the piston must be made smaller in diameter than the cylinder bore. The piston is then made a gas-tight fit in the cylinder by the use of several split cast iron rings. These are made a close fit in grooves machined in the piston sides and they spring outward to make firm contact with the cylinder walls.

Each piston is attached securely to the small end of a *connecting rod* by means of a *gudgeon pin*. This pin passes through both the small end of the rod and the piston, and is located centrally in the piston by

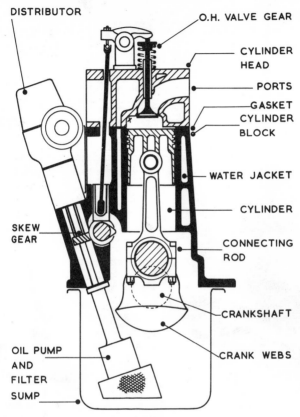

DISTRIBUTOR

O.H. VALVE GEAR

CYLINDER HEAD

PORTS

GASKET

CYLINDER BLOCK

WATER JACKET

CYLINDER

CONNECTING ROD

SKEW GEAR

CRANKSHAFT

CRANK WEBS

OIL PUMP AND FILTER

SUMP

Fig. 4.1   Engine layout

circlips. The large or 'big-end' of the connecting rod is bolted to a crankpin on the crankshaft and rotates on a whitemetal bearing.

The *crankshaft* is a very tough alloy steel forging which is arranged below, in line, and parallel with the cylinders. The crankshaft main journals rotate in whitemetal bearings fitted into the crankcase webs. A *crankpin* is arranged in line with each cylinder. The *crankcase* both supports and encloses the crankshaft, and in most engines the crankcase and cylinder block are cast as a one-piece unit.

The lower part of the crankcase is enclosed by a pressed steel or

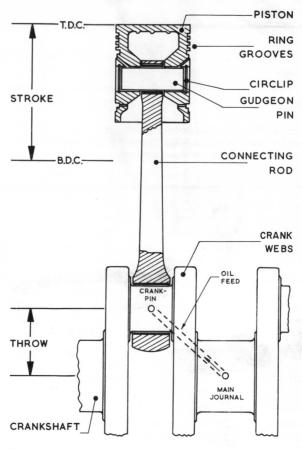

Fig. 4.2   Crank assembly

aluminium alloy sump which also acts as a tank for the engine lubricating oil.

A heavy cast iron or steel disc is bolted to the rear of the crankshaft. This disc is the *flywheel* and it makes the crankshaft revolve more evenly. It also provides a mounting and one driving face for the clutch unit. When the electric starter motor is operated its driving gear is automatically engaged with a ring of gear teeth on the outer diameter of the flywheel. In this way the rotation of the starter driving gear causes the crankshaft to be rotated to start the engine.

The *engine valves* are arranged in a straight line either above the cylinders or at one side of them, either in the cylinder head or in the top of the cylinder block. In the first arrangement they are classed as overhead valves (O.H.V.) and in the second arrangement as side valves (S.V.) (see Fig. 4.3).

The valve seats are fitted at the edges of the ports in the walls of the combustion chambers. The points of the sparking plugs are arranged to protrude slightly into the combustion chamber. The *cams* which open the valves are all arranged upon a single *camshaft* which is supported in plain holes in the crankcase webs. The camshaft is driven by chains or gears at half the speed of the crankshaft. The inlet and the exhaust valves are not kept open for the same lengths of time, neither are they opened and closed at the same moments in relation to the movement of the piston. The exhaust and inlet cams are therefore of different shapes and are arranged at different positions around the shaft. The camshaft is also fitted with a *skew gear* which drives the shafts of the lubricating oil pump and the ignition system distributor unit.

Each valve is supported in a guide and is held down to its seat by a strong spring, so closing the port. The spring is located at the end of the valve stem by a *retainer*. The valve is opened at the correct time, in relation to the motion of the piston, and is held open for the correct interval of time by the action of its cam. As the cam moves away from the valve, the valve is closed at the correct time by the action of its spring. The cam does not operate directly on to the valve but through an adjustable tappet in the side valve arrangement, and additionally a push-rod in the overhead valve arrangement. A hollow casting, approximating to the form of a tube, is bolted to the side of either the cylinder block or the cylinder head. This casting is the *inlet manifold* which directs the flow of the petrol and air mixture to each inlet port. It also provides a mounting for the carburettor and air cleaner. A casting of similar shape collects the exhaust gases and directs them to the exhaust pipe and silencer. These manifolds are usually bolted together at their centres to enable the exhaust manifold to supply a limited amount of heat to the inlet manifold. This is done to help in the vaporisation of the liquid petrol.

The *carburettor* is used to supply the correct quantity of petrol to suit

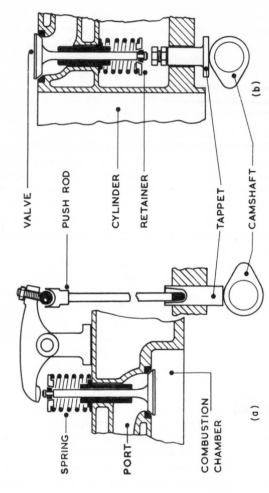

Fig. 4.3 Valve arrangements: (a) overhead (O.H.V.); (b) side (S.V.)

the amount of air entering the engine at any given moment. It must also convert liquid petrol into a vapour and mix it with air to form an explosive mixture.

When the mixture of petrol and air has been fully compressed in the combustion chamber and cylinder it is ignited by an electric spark. This occurs at or near the highest position reached by the piston on its compression stroke. A high voltage is needed to make a spark jump across the gap between the points of the sparking plug in the compressed mixture. The battery voltage is therefore stepped up or 'transformed' by the action of a transformer or *coil*. The high-voltage electricity produced is then directed to each sparking plug, in the correct sequence, by the distributor unit.

Friction is a force which always resists movement of one surface over another. It causes wear, produces heat and wastes power, so all the moving parts of the engine must be lubricated to reduce these effects. The *oil pump* is submerged in the oil held in the sump. The pump forces oil under a high pressure into the crankshaft main and big-end bearings, and the camshaft bearings, through holes drilled in the crankcase webs and crankshaft webs. Overhead valve operating gear is also lubricated by this high-pressure oil. The remaining engine parts are lubricated by oil splashed from the pressure-fed bearings.

Engine mountings

Allowance is made for a certain amount of engine vibration by supporting the engine, or sub-frame, on rubber cushions. These damp down the frequencies of the vibrations transmitted from the engine to the chassis and are usually two, three or four in number.

Engine mountings consist of a special form of rubber which may be arranged in shear, compression or torsion. The rubber must be resistant to oil and petrol and also to oxidation or ageing. A common form of mounting is a block of rubber which is sandwiched between two metal plates and securely attached to each by a chemical bonding process.

The functions of these mountings are:
(1) To support the weight of the engine in the chassis.
(2) To absorb the engine vibrations.
(3) To resist the turning of the engine unit in relation to the chassis, i.e. to resist the torque reaction forces which operate in the opposite direction of rotation from that of the crankshaft.

ENGINE OPERATION

Although vehicle engines are constructed and arranged in many different ways, the basic differences depend mainly upon the operating cycle of the engine. Petrol engines are operated using either a four-stroke or two-stroke cycle.

When a piston is at the upper limit of its travel in the cylinder it is said to be at the *top dead centre* or T.D.C. position. In this position the centres of the piston, gudgeon pin, connecting rod and crankweb lie on the centre line of the cylinder as observed from the front or rear of the engine.

Similarly the piston is said to be at *bottom dead centre* or B.D.C. when it is at the lower limit of its travel in the cylinder. The distance moved by the piston from one position to the other is called a *stroke*. The stroke of the piston is twice the *throw* of the crankshaft, which is the distance between the centres of the main bearing and the crankpin (see Fig. 4.2).

Four-stroke cycle

In this cycle the piston moves up and down the cylinder twice, each of the four strokes performing a different task. The cycle is completed in *two* complete revolutions of the crankshaft (see Fig. 4.4).

The four strokes, in their correct sequence, are: (1) induction, (2) compression, (3) power, (4) exhaust.

Induction. The inlet valve is opened a few degrees of crankshaft rotation before the piston reaches T.D.C. at the end of the exhaust stroke – and before the closing of the exhaust valve. This angle, where both valves are open at the same time, is known as *valve overlap* and its purpose is to allow the momentum of the escaping exhaust gas to help in drawing in the fresh charge of petrol and air mixture. The exhaust gases create a slight drop in pressure near the inlet port and start the fresh mixture moving into the cylinder. This results in a little extra weight of mixture being induced into the cylinder and so increases the power output of the engine. The exhaust valve is closed a few degrees after T.D.C.

As the piston is moved down the cylinder by the action of the crankshaft and connecting rod, it increases the effective volume of the cylinder and reduces the pressure inside the cylinder. The difference between this pressure and the higher atmospheric pressure outside the cylinder forces air to flow through the air cleaner and carburettor where

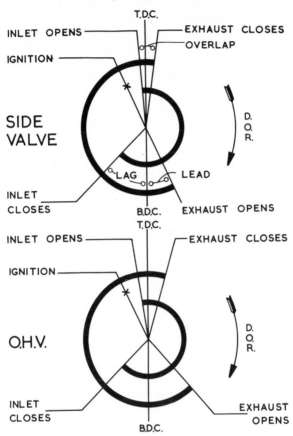

SIDE
VALVE

O.H.V.

Fig. 4.4   Timing diagrams

it is mixed with the correct mass of petrol. The mixture flows into the
cylinder at a very high speed and under a pressure of about 14 kN/m^2.
The mixture is also given a violent swirling motion.

Due to its momentum the mixture continues to flow into the cylinder
for a number of crankshaft degrees after the piston has passed over
B.D.C. and started to move up the cylinder on the compression stroke.
The inlet valve is closed after B.D.C. and this delay is known as *valve*

lag. Lag also allows a little extra mass of mixture to be induced into the cylinder.

Compression. As the piston moves up towards T.D.C. with both valves closed, the swirling mixture is compressed into a much smaller volume, the degree of compression depending on the *compression ratio* (C.R.) of the engine. For a C.R. of 7 : 1 the mixture will be under a pressure of about 1240 kN/m² and its temperature will rise to about 400 °C.

A few crankshaft degrees before the piston reaches T.D.C. the compressed, heated and swirling mixture is ignited by an electric spark.

There is always a time lag or delay period between the occurrence of the spark and the full expansion of the air in the mixture. The spark is therefore timed to occur before the piston reaches T.D.C. so all the petrol is burning and the air is fully heated and expanding as the piston passes over T.D.C. and reaches the position from which it can exert the maximum force on the crankshaft. The mixture always takes the same time to reach its maximum pressure after ignition, so the burning must be started earlier as the piston speeds are increased, i.e. the spark must occur farther and farther before T.D.C. as the engine speed is increased. This is called *ignition advance*.

Power. As soon as the spark has ignited the mixture, it burns very rapidly and the heat energy released causes a very rapid expansion of the air. It is the expansion of the *air* which produces the power of the engine. For a very short time the temperature of the mixture may be over 2000 °C while the pressure rises to about 5200 kN/m². This pressure is exerted over the total area of the piston crown, and the total resulting force of about 2 tonnes forces the piston down the cylinder to rotate the crankshaft through the action of the connecting rod and crankpin.

As the piston moves down the cylinder the pressure falls rapidly and the exhaust valve is opened before B.D.C.

Exhaust. At the moment the exhaust valve is opened the pressure in the cylinder has fallen to about 550 kN/m². As the exhaust valve opens fully the gases leave the cylinder under a pressure of about 20 kN/m², at a very high speed, and at a temperature of about 800 °C.

The early opening of the exhaust valve, known as *valve lead*, is used to enable the gases to escape under their own pressure. This is possible because their useful power has already been transferred to the crankshaft and, by expelling the gases more speedily, the back pressure on the piston is reduced as it passes over B.D.C. and moves up the cylinder again.

The exhausting of the gases is completed by the upward movement of the piston. As it approaches T.D.C. the inlet valve is opened to start the next cycle. The exhaust valve is then closed a few degrees after T.D.C. on the following induction stroke.

Ineffective crank angle. Valve lead, lag and overlap are used to induce the greatest possible mass of mixture to enter the cylinders and to clear out the spent gases as quickly as possible, in both cases to increase the power of the engine. These timings can be used because, at T.D.C. and B.D.C., there are a few degrees of crankshaft rotation where the movement of the crankshaft has such a slight effect on the movement of the piston that the gases are not affected. This 'dead' movement is called *ineffective crank angle*.

The two-stroke cycle

Construction

The single-cylinder two-stroke engine has no valves, the sides of the piston being employed to open and close ports in the cylinder walls at the correct moments (see Fig. 4.5). The single crankpin and piston and connecting rod assembly is counterbalanced by weights on the opposite side of the crankshaft. The carburettor is bolted to a port opening into the crankcase while the exhaust port is directly above the inlet port. A transfer or by-pass port is arranged from the crankcase to the cylinder at a point opposite the exhaust port but slightly nearer to B.D.C. The engine lubricating oil is mixed with the petrol and the mixture is ignited by an electric spark. This system of lubrication is called 'petroil' and the proportions are 0·25 litres of oil to 4 litres of petrol.

Note. When studying operating cycles it is more useful to follow the course of a fresh charge of mixture through the cycle than to concentrate on mechanical details.

Cycle of operations

This cycle is more difficult to understand than the four-stroke cycle because the piston performs two different tasks during each of its two strokes. Two quantities of mixture are in the engine at the same time and the mixture is compressed twice before it is ignited. During the down stroke the first charge is burning and expanding above the piston and providing power to rotate the shaft. The piston is also

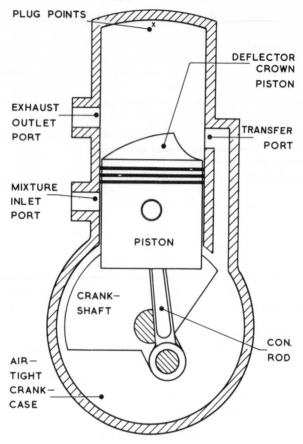

Fig. 4.5   Two-stroke engine

subjecting the second charge to its first compression in the air-tight crankcase.

Upward stroke. When the piston is at B.D.C. the inlet port is closed and the exhaust and transfer ports are open. Exhaust gases are leaving the cylinder and a compressed charge of fresh mixture is entering at the transfer port on the opposite side of the cylinder. The piston crown is so shaped that the fresh mixture is deflected to the top of the cylinder while the exhaust gases are directed to the exhaust port. As the piston moves up the cylinder, it seals off the transfer and exhaust ports and its continued movement increases the effective volume of the air-tight crankcase. This reduces the pressure inside the crankcase and, when the piston uncovers the inlet port, the difference between this reduced pressure and the higher atmospheric pressure causes air to flow through the carburettor and mixture to enter the crankcase through the inlet port. The swirling petrol and oil mist lubricates the moving parts as the crankshaft rotates.

As the piston approaches T.D.C. the mixture in the cylinder above the piston is compressed for the second time and is then ignited.

Down stroke. The expansion of the burning mixture forces the piston to move down the cylinder and so rotate the crankshaft. At the same time the descending piston closes the inlet port and begins to reduce the effective volume of the crankcase. This action compresses the mixture in the crankcase until the piston begins to uncover the transfer port. The compressed mixture then forces its way from the crankcase through the transfer passage and up into the cylinder to start the cycle of operations again. The exhaust gases leave the cylinder as the exhaust port is uncovered.

Comparison of cycles

If a comparison were to be made between the two-stroke engine and a four-stroke engine of the same bore and stroke, running at the same speed, it would appear logical to expect that the two-stroke with twice the number of power strokes per revolution of the crankshaft would develop twice the power. In fact the two-stroke produces only 50% to 60% more power.

The difference is explained by the following:

(1) The two-stroke has twice as many power strokes in the same time as the four-stroke and therefore operates at higher temperatures. The mixture itself is heated more and the volume weighs less. This effect combined with the very short inlet-port-open period results in the incomplete charging of the crankcase with mixture.

(2) Although the piston has a deflector crown, some of the mixture reaching the cylinder passes across the piston and escapes with the exhaust gases during the period in which the transfer and exhaust ports are both open.

The incomplete initial charging of the crankcase, and the later losses of mixture through the exhaust port, result in the two-stroke engine producing lower expansion pressures than the four-stroke and therefore less than twice the power.

Multi-cylinder engines

For given piston speeds and under given cylinder pressures there are two methods by which more power may be obtained at the crankshaft. One method is to increase the diameter of the cylinder. The second method is to use a greater number of smaller diameter cylinders.

A single-cylinder four-stroke engine has only one power stroke in every two crankshaft revolutions so the crankshaft does not rotate smoothly, i.e. its torque or turning movement is uneven. If more and smaller cylinders are added not only will the power at the crankshaft be increased but the torque will be much more even. A further point about this method is that the weight increase of the engine will be roughly in proportion to the power increase.

If a larger diameter of cylinder is used it will be found that the weight of the engine increases at a faster rate than the power increase obtained. This is because the volume and strength of the engine must also be increased.

Power to weight ratio

The engine designer tries to obtain the largest possible power output from the smallest possible weight of engine, i.e. the largest ratio of power to weight. A comparison can be made between different engines by dividing their power output (kilowatts) by their weight in kilogrammes. Increasing power by the use of larger diameter cylinders results in a low power to weight ratio, so vehicle engines use larger numbers of small diameter cylinders instead of one or two large cylinders.

The arrangement of the cylinders is governed by the difficulties of obtaining an acceptable degree of balance.

ENGINE BALANCE

The three main causes of engine vibration or unbalance are:
(1) The torque reaction forces.
(2) The lack of balance of the crankshaft itself, and of the piston and connecting rod assembly.

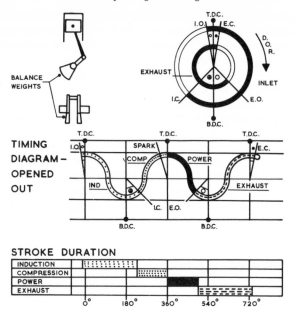

TIMING DIAGRAM – OPENED OUT

STROKE DURATION

	0°	180°	360°	540°	720°
INDUCTION					
COMPRESSION					
POWER					
EXHAUST					

Fig. 4.6 Timing diagram

(3) The regularity or otherwise of the power impulses (even or uneven intervals of crankshaft rotation between the power strokes).

Any engine which is delivering torque (i.e. working against a load or resistance) has a tendency to rotate bodily in a direction opposite from that of the torque. This tendency is called *torque reaction* and it must be limited by the mounting arrangements of the power unit. The torque reaction will vary with the torque acting on the crankshaft.

When the crankshaft assembly is rotating, the forces due to the masses of the crankpin, connecting rod and piston are not balanced by equal and opposite forces. This produces a vibration in the assembly which is transmitted to the whole engine. The magnitude of this vibration depends largely upon the masses, numbers and arrangement of the crankpins and the piston and connecting rod assemblies.

The crankshaft itself can be balanced exactly by arranging counter-weights. These are equal in mass to the crankpin and are fitted on the opposite side of the shaft from the crankpin.

The masses of the piston and connecting rod cannot be exactly counterbalanced in this way as the position of their centre of gravity is continually changing. The effect of their lack of balance can be reduced, however, by the use of a relatively long connecting rod, and by the use of a light-weight piston and connecting rod. A further reduction of vibration can also be obtained by slightly increasing the mass of the crankshaft counterweights.

The torque delivered by the crankshaft is derived from the power stroke which forces the crankpin to rotate about the centre of the shaft. As the shaft is being forced round against a resistance, it is subjected to a torsional stress, or twist, which will fluctuate from a high to a low value as the power strokes occur. The fluctuating stress and torque produce their own vibration, the severity of which will depend upon the design of the crankshaft and the frequency of the power impulses. The greater the number of power impulses in each crankshaft revolution the smoother the torque.

Single cylinder Fig. 4.7
The simplest form of petrol engine is the single-cylinder design operating on either the two- or four-stroke cycle. The crankshaft has one crankpin and two main journals, and may be made as a one-piece forging of alloy steel or as a bolted-together assembly. The first type will rotate in plain whitemetalled bearings but the construction of the second type permits the use of a parallel roller bearing for the connecting rod big-end and ball or taper-roller thrust bearings for the main journals. These types of bearings have a point or line contact and therefore the losses due to friction are much less than in plain bearings.

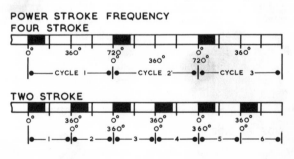

Fig. 4.7   Single-cylinder power strokes

When operating on the four-stroke cycle the crankshaft receives one power impulse in every 720° of its rotation, and one power impulse in every 360° of rotation when operating under the two-stroke cycle. The crankshaft torque is therefore uneven and a heavy flywheel must be fitted to carry the crankshaft over the non-powered or idle strokes. The flywheel may be incorporated into the crankshaft webs.

The balance of a single-cylinder engine is poor because of all the previously described causes. In practice the crankpin (rotating mass) is counterbalanced exactly by masses mounted on the crank web/fly-wheels. The piston and connecting rod (reciprocating mass) cannot be counterbalanced exactly but a compromise is arranged in which the crank web/flywheel masses are increased by about two-thirds of the piston and connecting rod mass. This reduces the vibration to a level which is acceptable for stationary engines and motor-cycles but not for motor-cars.

Note that the power stroke does not result in a sustained force on the crankpin but is instead a sudden, short, and rapidly reducing force.

Twin cylinders

In addition to providing more power than single-cylinder designs, the

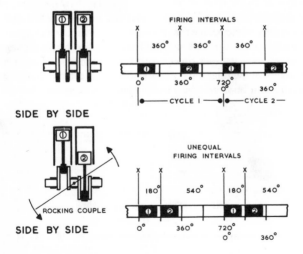

Fig. 4.8   Twin-cylinder arrangement

twin cylinders also provide a more even torque. The two cylinders may be arranged side by side, or horizontally opposed to each other, or in the form of a vee (see Fig. 4.9).

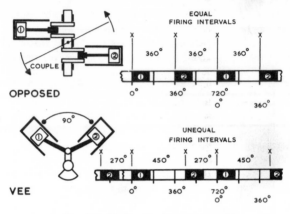

Fig. 4.9   Twin-cylinder arrangement

Side by side

Two different crankshaft designs can be used with this arrangement of the cylinders. In one design the crankpins are parallel to each other and on the same side of the shaft. In effect this is two single-cylinder engines, the pistons moving up and down together although they are on different strokes. The overall engine balance is poor because the reciprocating masses cannot be counterbalanced. When this engine is operated on the four-stroke cycle there is one power stroke during each 360° of crankshaft rotation, so the crankshaft torque is smoother than that of the single cylinder. The firing intervals are equal. This arrangement is often used in motor-cycle engines.

In the alternative crankshaft arrangement the crankpins are 180° apart on opposite sides of the shaft. The reciprocating masses partly balance each other but a rocking couple is produced, because they cannot be arranged to exactly oppose each other, thus causing the engine to move like a see-saw about the centre of the crankshaft length. This is explained by the fact that for a given number of degrees of crankshaft rotation a piston will move farther down the cylinder from top dead centre than it will move up from bottom dead centre (see Fig. 4.10).

The two piston movements cannot therefore balance each other but the overall engine balance is better than in the previous arrangement. The power impulses occur every 180° and 540° of crankshaft rotation; that is the firing intervals are unequal, and the torque is not so smooth, as the two power impulses occur one after the other, and are followed by two idle strokes.

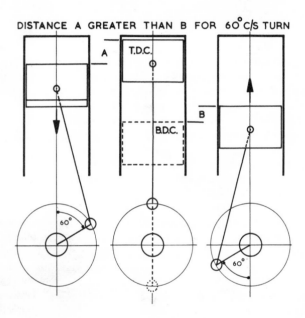

Fig. 4.10   Angularity

Horizontally opposed twin

This is sometimes known as the flat twin. The cylinders are arranged 180° apart and on opposite sides of the shaft. The crankpins are similarly arranged. The pistons move up and down their cylinders together and their reciprocating masses almost balance each other. The rocking motion caused by the impossibility of arranging the two cylinders exactly opposite each other can be very much reduced by the use of narrow roller-type main bearings. The firing intervals are equal and the torque is smoother than the opposed crank side-by-side arrangement. These features, plus the very good overall balance, enable this type of engine to operate at speeds of up to 6000 revolutions per minute.

Vee twin

In the vee twins the cylinders are arranged at various angles to each other, usually between 40° and 90°. Both connecting rods are attached to the single crankpin and the rotating mass is counterbalanced by the crank webs. The balance of the engine is improved as the angle between the cylinders is made closer to 90°. The 90° twin has excellent balance but it has the disadvantage that the firing interval is unequal, being 270° and 450°. As the angle between the cylinders is reduced, the firing intervals become more equal and the torque smoother but the balance is made worse. For most purposes the better balance is of more value than equal firing intervals.

Three cylinders, Fig. 4.11

In this arrangement the cylinders are arranged in a line and the crankpins are arranged at 120° intervals around the shaft (see Fig. 4.11). The overall balance is only moderate because no two pistons can oppose each other exactly at any moment. The power impulses are evenly spaced at 240° intervals and the torque is smoother than that of the twin-cylinder arrangements.

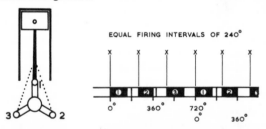

Fig. 4.11   Three-cylinder in-line arrangement

Four cylinders

In-line, Fig. 4.12

The most popular arrangement for use in the small and medium sizes of car is the four-cylinder in-line engine.

In these engines the cylinders are arranged in a line above a flat, four-throw crankshaft. Three main bearings have normally been employed but modern designs are using five-bearing crankshafts. Each of these bearings is narrower than the previous type so the shaft can be given more support without it being made excessively long. Pistons 1 and 4

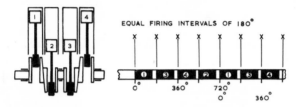

EQUAL FIRING INTERVALS OF 180°

Fig. 4.12   Four-cylinder in-line arrangement

will be at top dead centre together while pistons 2 and 3 will be at bottom dead centre together. The pairs will move up and down together but each cylinder will be on a different stroke. For example, if number 1 is on its induction stroke, its piston will be moving down and so will piston 4. The only other down stroke is that of power so piston 4 will be on its power stroke. Similarly, if number 2 cylinder is on its exhaust stroke, then number 3 must be on its compression stroke.

In this arrangement the firing interval is regular, one power impulse occurring in every 180° of crankshaft rotation. Although the torque is continuous it fluctuates in value as one power stroke is dying away as the next is building up. A flywheel is still required to smooth out the torque but it need only be light in mass. As this engine is similar to two two-cylinder engines arranged end to end, the two rocking couples neutralise each other and the overall balance is good. It is not completely balanced, however, because the reciprocating forces do not exactly oppose each other. The effect of these forces is much reduced by the use of light-weight pistons and connecting rods.

The firing order is either 1, 3, 4, 2, or 1, 2, 4, 3.

Opposed, Fig. 4.13

A well-known engine arranged in this manner is the air-cooled Volks-wagen. The cylinders are arranged horizontally in pairs on each side of a flat four crankshaft. Engine balance is superior to that of the in-line arrangement. The firing intervals are regular and one power impulse occurs in every 180° of crankshaft rotation. The torque is smooth and a light-weight flywheel only is required. The Volkswagen firing order is 1, 4, 3, 2, the cylinders being numbered according to the position of the connecting rods on the crankshaft.

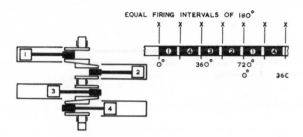

Fig. 4.13   Four-cylinder opposed arrangement

Square four, Fig. 4.14

Four cylinders can also be arranged to form a square. In effect this is two two-cylinder, in-line engines in which the crankshafts are inter-connected by gears. In one motor-cycle design the shafts were arranged across the frame and the clutch was driven from the end of the rear shaft.

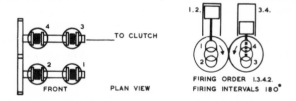

Fig. 4.14   Four-cylinder square arrangement

Vee-four, Fig. 4.15

This arrangement is similar to two two-cylinder vee engines having a common crankshaft. Where the vee angle is narrow, about 20°, a two-throw crankshaft is used.

In a modern vee-four the cylinders are arranged in staggered pairs

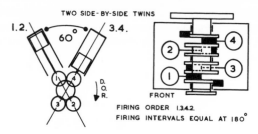

Fig. 4.15   Four-cylinder vee arrangement

over a single crankshaft. The angle between the pairs is 60° and the crankshaft is a rather unusual type. Two crankpins are arranged 60° apart at one side and end of the shaft while the remaining two are 60° apart on the opposite end and side. The shaft itself is balanced by means of weighted webs, assisted by weights in the pulley and flywheel. The rocking couple which is produced by this crankpin and cylinder arrangement is counteracted by the use of a crankshaft-driven balance shaft. This has eccentric weights which produce another couple of equal size in the opposite direction. The firing order, or sequence, is 1, 3, 4, 2, and the firing interval is 180°.

The square and narrow vee-four cylinder arrangements have been used successfully in motor-cycles and in a very few cars. The arrangement of the cylinders in staggered pairs results in a shorter and more compact engine than the in-line four.

The balance of each of the four-cylinder arrangements is similar to that of the twin-cylinder types but is generally slightly better. The four-cylinder torque is much smoother because of the larger number of power strokes per revolution.

THE PETROL SUPPLY SYSTEM

The engine is a device which converts heat energy, derived from the petrol, into mechanical energy. In this form the energy can be used to propel the vehicle.

The petrol supply system (Fig. 4.16) includes the carburettor, the lift pump, the tank, and suitable pipes and filters. The petrol supply is usually carried at the rear of the vehicle, in a pressed-steel tank which generally holds sufficient petrol for about 480 km of continuous

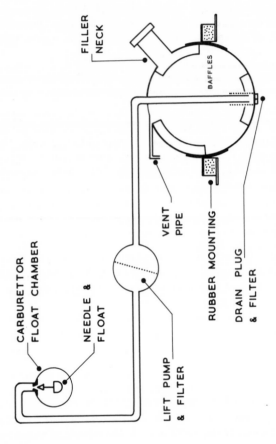

Fig. 4.16   Petrol supply system

motoring. The tank contains baffles to prevent surging of the petrol. Because the tank is below the level of the engine-mounted carburettor the petrol must be pumped forward and up to the height of the carburettor float chamber. The lift pump which does this may be operated mechanically or electrically. In both types the delivery pressure is derived from the release of a spring, which has first been compressed mechanically or electrically. The pumping pressure is usually about $20 \, kN/m^2$.

The lift pump supplies petrol to the float chamber by first reducing its own internal pressure below atmospheric. This causes petrol to flow from the tank into the pump chamber. Supply from the tank is then cut off by a valve and the lift pump then exerts a pressure above atmospheric, which forces petrol into the carburettor float chamber. The varying demand of the float chamber is controlled by a float-operated needle valve which stops the pump delivery when the correct level of petrol is reached. The pumps are designed to idle when the float needle valve is closed to its seat.

THE SIMPLE CARBURETTOR

Function

The carburettor is used to convert liquid petrol into a vapour and then to mix it with air to form the very rapid burning charge needed by the engine. The normal, or chemically correct, composition of the mixture is 15 parts of air to 1 petrol – by mass. The proportions are based on mass because a volume of warm air has less mass than the same volume at a lower temperature.

Arrangement

The simple carburettor consists of two main sections, one dealing with air supply and the other dealing with petrol supply (see Fig. 4.17).

Air supply. This section includes the main air tube, the throttle valve and the venturi. The end of the air tube containing the throttle valve is bolted to the flange of the inlet manifold. The throttle valve is a flat disc which is mounted upon a spindle connected to the accelerator pedal in such a way that, when the pedal is depressed, the valve is turned to open the air passage into the engine, so controlling the flow of air through the main tube. The *venturi* is a shaped restriction piece fitted into the tube above the throttle valve.

When air flows through the tube and venturi, Fig. 4.17(a), a drop in pressure occurs in the centre of the venturi, the drop in pressure increasing as the air speed is increased. This action is known as *venturi*

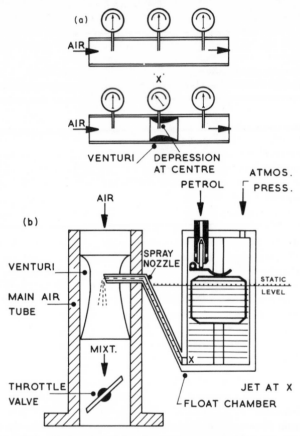

Fig. 4.17   Carburation: (a) action of the venturi; (b) petrol supply

action and is due to a conversion of energy. The air moving through the tube has a certain total amount of energy which is the sum of its movement and pressure energies. As the air enters the venturi the restriction to its flow increases its speed and therefore its movement energy. The total amount of energy is unchanged so the increasing of the movement energy causes a reduction of the pressure energy, i.e. a drop in pressure.

Petrol supply. This section consists of the float chamber and the petrol-spraying nozzle, Fig. 4.17(b). These two are connected by a pipe or by ducts drilled through the carburettor body. When petrol fills the float chamber and nozzle the level in each will be the same because the same atmospheric pressure is acting on the surface of each. The tip of the nozzle is arranged to be slightly above the level of the petrol.

The two sections are connected together by fitting the spray nozzle tip into the centre of the venturi.

Action

As the engine pistons move on their induction strokes they create a depression in their cylinders and in the inlet manifold (a *depression* is a pressure less than that of the atmosphere). The difference between the outside atmospheric pressure and the depression inside the manifold forces air to pass through the carburettor air tube. When the air passes through the venturi a depression is created around the tip of the spray nozzle. The atmospheric pressure acting on the petrol in the float chamber is now higher than the pressure on the petrol in the nozzle, and the difference between the two pressures forces petrol to flow from the float chamber and out of the nozzle into the air stream. The shape of the nozzle tip, the pressure drop and the speed of the air all help to break the liquid petrol up into very tiny drops. These absorb heat from the air and the metal of the air tube walls, and are changed into vapour.

Increasing the air speed by opening the throttle increases the pressure difference between the float chamber and the nozzle and results in more petrol being delivered. Reducing the air speed by closing the throttle reduces the pressure difference and so reduces the amount of petrol being delivered.

Disadvantages

The main disadvantage of the simple carburettor is that although the quantities (volume) of mixture can be accurately controlled, the strength (proportions of petrol and air – by mass) of the mixture cannot be controlled.

This is because petrol (liquid) and air (vapour) have different flow characteristics. The mass of petrol delivered per second depends upon the pressure difference which in turn depends upon the air speed. As the throttle is opened the mass of petrol delivered per second will increase in step with the increase in air speed.

When the throttle is opened the air speed is increased but the density (mass per given volume) of the moving air is reduced. The volume of air passing per second is increased but the mass per second is reduced. The proportion of air in the mixture is therefore reduced and the *mixture strength* is steadily increased as the engine speed rises.

The simple carburettor provides a rich mixture at high air speeds, which weakens off as the air speeds are reduced until somewhere in the medium speed range the mixture is the correct 15 : 1. Below these speeds the mixture is weakened off until it becomes so weak that the engine cannot produce enough power to keep running.

While it is true that the engine needs a slightly rich mixture to develop its full power, the mixtures provided by the simple carburettor are excessively rich. To some extent this can be counteracted by fitting a petrol restrictor or jet between the float chamber and the spray nozzle but the simple carburettor can only enable the engine to develop its maximum power, for a given petrol consumption, when the engine is operated in a fairly limited range of engine speeds. As excessive loads will reduce engine speeds the loads acting against an engine fitted with a simple carburettor must also be limited.

5   The Compression-ignition Engine

The construction and operation of the spark-ignition engine has been described in Chapter 4. Another widely used type is the compression-ignition engine, commonly called the diesel engine. The components of the two types of engine, and their arrangement, are very similar but as they have to withstand higher pressures and larger forces each individual component of the compression-ignition (C.I.) engine has to be stronger and therefore heavier.

In the C.I. engine a charge of **air only** is subjected to such a high degree of compression that its temperature rises to about 550 °C. Fuel oil, in the form of a spray of very minute drops, is then forced into the hot air where it vaporises and burns, without being ignited by an electric spark.

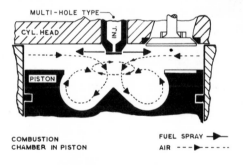

Fig. 5.1   Direct injection

The combustion chamber may be formed in the piston crown (direct injection) or in the cylinder head offset from the bore (indirect or separate chamber injection). These chambers are specially shaped to cause the air to move about violently and so break up and mix with the spray of fuel oil very quickly. This speed of mixing is very important to

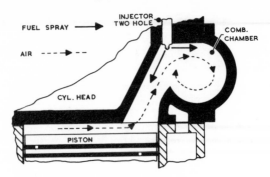

Fig. 5.2   Indirect injection

the efficiency of combustion. The expansion of the air produces a sustained pressure on the piston, which converts it into the force which rotates the crankshaft.

C.I. engines may operate under either the four-stroke or the two-stroke cycle.

Four-stroke cycle operation

Induction

The inlet valve is opened before T.D.C. on the exhaust stroke and before the exhaust valve is closed (valve overlap). **Air only** is forced into the cylinder by the difference in pressure between the air outside the cylinder (atmospheric) and the reduced pressure inside the cylinder (depression) resulting from the downward movement of the piston, following the closure of the exhaust valve after T.D.C.

Compression

The air entering the cylinder is made to swirl and the inlet valve is closed after the piston has passed over B.D.C. (valve lag). The upward movement of the piston reduces the volume of the air by somewhere between 14 and 22 times, i.e. the compression ratio is between 14 : 1 and 22 : 1. Under this degree of compression (2750 to 4140 kN/m^2) the temperature of the air rises to about 550 °C. This is well above the temperature at which the fuel oil will self-ignite, so when the fuel is injected and the spray is broken up burning commences very quickly.

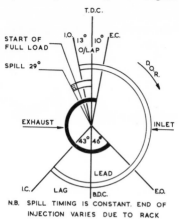

Fig. 5.3   C.I. timings

Injection or power stroke

Just before T.D.C. on the compression stroke, fuel oil is forced (injected) into the dense (highly compressed) and heated air in the combustion chamber. The burning continues – after injection has ceased – for about two-thirds of the power stroke. The resulting continuous expansion as the piston moves down provides the very strong and sustained power stroke which results in the crankshaft torque of the C.I. engine being much smoother than that of the spark-ignition engine.

Exhaust

The exhaust valve is opened before the piston reaches B.D.C. (valve lead) to allow the waste gases to leave the cylinder under their own pressure. As the piston moves upward after B.D.C. the remaining gases are swept out before it.

Note. As in the spark-ignition engine, valve lead, lag and overlap are used to obtain the greatest possible mass of air in the cylinder (highest volumetric efficiency) and the quickest and most complete scavenge of the exhaust gases.

C.I. fuel

The fuels used by C.I. engines fitted into vehicles is a light oil composed of hydrogen, carbon, oxygen and sulphur. These fuels do not vaporise and self-ignite at such low temperatures as petrol (lower flash point) so the risk of fire is much reduced. The most important quality of these fuels is probably their ability to self-ignite rapidly after being injected into the dense and heated air in the combustion chamber. The ignition quality of different fuels is indicated by their Cetane rating, a good fuel having a rating of 60 or above and the quality reducing down to about 30 Cetane. Unlike petrol, C.I. fuels can adequately lubricate the component parts of their pumps, etc.

Fuel system

Towards the end of the compression stroke the combustion chamber contains air under a high pressure and for the fuel to enter at all it must be injected under a much higher pressure. The liquid fuel must also enter in the form of a spray of very minute liquid drops, and these drops must reach (penetrate) to all parts of the chamber. These factors necessitate the fuel being injected at pressures of between 7600 and 24 000 kN/m^2.

The very high pressure is obtained by the use of an engine-driven plunger pump of special design, and the spray is obtained by the use of an injector nozzle with very small holes through which the high pressure forces the fuel. The injection pump also controls the amount of fuel injected to match up to the mass of air entering the combustion chamber, i.e. the pump meters as well as pressurises the fuel.

Note. As the injection pump and the injector have to operate under very high pressures the clearances between their moving parts are extremely small. It is essential that the fuel oil be kept both very clean and free from all traces of water. Failure to keep the oil clean in both bulk storage tanks and vehicle tanks, and failure to change the filters regularly, will result in the very rapid wear and possible destruction of the pumps and injectors.

Layout

The fuel system consists of a tank, one or more very fine paper filters, a lift pump and an injection pump and injector for each cylinder. Pipes connect the various units as shown in Fig. 5.4, special high-pressure pipes with welded unions and thick walls being used to connect the injectors to their pumps.

The tank is usually situated at the side or rear of the chassis and is arranged on rubber mountings. It has a vent pipe and internal baffles and it may be fitted with a gauge, reading in litres. The lift pump is used to transfer fuel from the tank to the injection pump and it may be driven from the injection pump or directly from the engine. The paper or fabric filters are arranged between the lift and the injection pumps. The

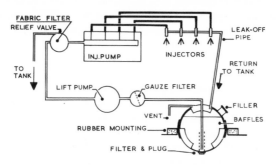

Fig. 5.4   C.I. engine fuel system

injection pumps are driven from the engine by their own camshaft and the pumping strokes are timed to the engine pistons. The injectors are fitted into the cylinder head such that their nozzle tips protrude slightly into the combustion chambers.

Operation

As the engine crankshaft is rotated a depression is created in the chamber of the lift pump. The pressure difference between the chamber and the higher (atmospheric) pressure in the tank, causes the fuel to flow from the tank into the pump chamber. As the crankshaft continues to rotate the pump then applies a higher pressure than atmospheric to the fuel and forces it through the filters to the gallery of the injection pumps. An accurately measured quantity of fuel is then subjected to a very high pressure by one of the injection pumps and is directed, in firing sequence, to its injector just as its cylinder is approaching the end of its compression stroke. The fuel leaving the pump enters a pipe-line which is already full, and the resulting pressure increase opens the injector needle to allow the fuel to be sprayed into the combustion chamber in the form of very tiny liquid drops. Due to the very high pressures used some fuel always escapes back past the injector needle valve. This fuel is collected by the leak-off pipes and is returned either to the tank or to the intake side of the fine filter.

C.A.V. injection pump
Function
The injection pump is used to:
(1) Build up a pressure high enough to force the fuel, in a finely atomised spray, into the combustion chamber against the pressure of the highly compressed and heated air.
(2) Measure out the fuel in minutely accurate quantities which must be varied to suit the mass of air entering the cylinders, i.e. to suit the speed and load requirements of the engine.
(3) Deliver the fuel to the injectors in the correct firing sequence and at the correct intervals of crankshaft rotation.

As previously mentioned one injection pump and one injector is required for each cylinder. In multi-cylinder engines the pumps are fitted into one housing and are driven by a single camshaft. The descriptions which follow relate to one injection pump only.

Construction
The main parts of the pump are the plunger and the barrel. Together these are called an element. The top of the barrel is sealed off by a delivery valve which has its own bore and seat. The plunger is forced to move up the barrel by a tappet and cam, and is returned by a spring and retainer. The barrel is enclosed by a sleeve which can be turned in either direction through the action of a gear quadrant clamped to it and engaging with a gear rack. The rack is moved by the accelerator pedal via a speed and load governor, or over-riding control. The top of the barrel has drilled ports which connect it to the gallery filled with fuel by the lift pump.

Pressurising
The plunger is grooved horizontally and vertically, the lower face of the plunger being the sealing or pressure face. The volume between this face and the delivery valve is filled by fuel at all times. The plunger also has a helical or spiralling groove which extends from a point near the top of the vertical groove to a point on the upper edge of the horizontal groove about 180° away. Fuel enters the barrel through two opposed ports arranged in the gallery pipe or bore. The top of the barrel is sealed

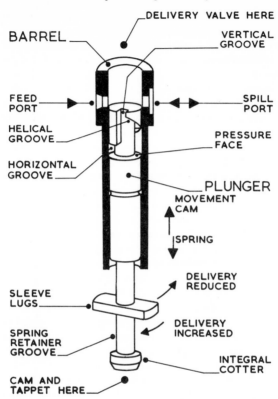

Fig. 5.5.   C.A.V. element

by a spring-loaded delivery valve of the non-return type, and is connected by a pipe to the body of the injector. Note that the pipe and the injector are permanently filled by fuel under a pressure just less than that needed to operate the injector.

When the cam and tappet force the plunger to move up the barrel the fuel in the barrel is displaced back into the gallery until the two ports are covered by the sides of the plunger. As this occurs the fuel in the barrel is completely enclosed. Further plunger movement reduces the volume and so increases the pressure acting upon the fuel (a fluid cannot be compressed). As soon as the pressure in the barrel exceeds that in the pipe-line and injector the delivery valve is forced from its seat and so compresses its spring. The instant the delivery valve opens the higher pressure is transmitted through the fuel to the injector and its needle valve is forced from its seat to allow fuel to be sprayed into the combustion chamber.

Continued plunger movement forces fuel from the barrel into the pipe, and an equivalent quantity from the injector. The spraying, therefore, continues until the helical groove is aligned with the spill port in the barrel. At the instant this occurs the fuel is no longer enclosed, the pressure in the barrel drops, the delivery valve is closed by its spring, the injector needle valve is snapped shut by its spring, and spraying ceases. Further movement of the plunger simply displaces fuel back into the gallery.

Metering

The helical groove is made to uncover the spill port at different stages of the plunger's upward movement by turning the plunger relative to the port, so varying the quantity of fuel forced into the pipe-line and also out of the injector. This is obtained by the use of the sleeve and quadrant, their movement being caused by the rack and transmitted via slots to the plunger. An anticlockwise turn reduces the volume of fuel injected and a clockwise turn increases the volume injected. When the plunger is turned to align the vertical groove with the feed port the pump will make no delivery at all as the fuel cannot be enclosed. This is the 'cut-off' position used to stop the engine.

Delivery valve

The delivery valve is designed to:

(a) act as a non-return valve during pump delivery, and

(b) act as an anti-dribble device as pump delivery ceases.

It is essential that the start and end of injection be clean and sharp actions, free from hesitation. The immediate start of injection is ensured by always having the pipe and injector full of fuel just below injection pressure. The clean-cut end of injection is ensured by the design of the valve, the plain portion acting as a small plunger pump as it enters its bore, thus increasing the effective volume of the pipe and suddenly reducing the pressure to enable the injector needle to close down to its seat in one rapid movement.

Construction

Below the spring shoulder the valve has a bevel face, a plain cylindrical portion and a fluted guide portion. These features are separated by grooves, and the valve has its own bore and seating fitted above th~ barrel of the element.

Operation

Start of delivery: The valve is held to its seat by the high pressure trapped in the injector and pipe-line, and by its spring. When the plunger upward movement produces a higher pressure this acting on the under-face of the plain portion of the valve (via the flutes), forces the valve to lift. At the instant the upper edge of the plain portion clears the bore the higher pressure acts through the fuel to open the injector needle and, therefore, the spraying commences.

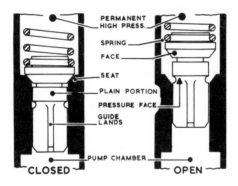

Fig. 5.6   Delivery valve

End of delivery: When the helical groove of the plunger uncovers the spill port the pressure below the valve is immediately reduced, and the valve is closed by its spring. As the lower edge of the plain portion enters the bore the pipe and injector are sealed off from the barrel, so trapping a high pressure in them as injection ceases. The movement of the plain portion down its bore then increases the effective volume of the pipe, and so reduces the pressure just enough to allow the injector spring to close its needle valve to its seat, without it bouncing open due to pressure surge (like water hammer in house pipes). The bevel face of the delivery valve then closes to its seat to retain the high pressure in the pipe and injector. The plain portion of the valve is therefore responsible for the elimination of the fault known as injector 'dribble'.

The injector
Function
The injector is used to:
(1) Introduce fuel oil into the combustion chamber under a very high pressure (7600 to 24 000 kN/m^2, depending upon type).
(2) Convert the liquid fuel into a very finely atomised spray of a shape and size suited to the design of combustion chamber.
(3) Direct the spray or sprays to the correct point in the combustion chamber so it may be very quickly broken up and mixed with the highly compressed and heated air swirling violently around.

Construction
Essentially the injector is an accurately machined needle valve which is forced from its seat by a suddenly increased pressure, and returned to its seat by a spring when the increased pressure is suddenly reduced.

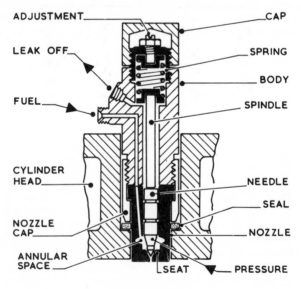

Fig. 5.7   Injector

Below the seat are one, two, or four very small holes through which the fuel is forced into the combustion chamber. The combination of a small hole and a very high pressure converts the liquid fuel into very, very small drops, the shape of the hole determining the size and shape of the spray.

One type of injector is illustrated in Fig. 5.7. The valve has a conical sealing face and a conical lifting or pressure face. The loading of the needle by the spring is adjustable, and this loading determines the pressure needed for correct injection, *not* the loading of the delivery valve.

Note. In all work relating to C.I. injection equipment very great care must be taken to ensure absolute cleanliness and freedom from careless handling.

The two-stroke C.I. engine

The disadvantages of the two-stroke, spark-ignition engine do not apply to the two-stroke, compression-ignition engine. As the C.I. engine induces air only, and not air mixed with fuel, it can produce more power from the burning of the same mass of fuel and it does not waste fuel when the inlet and exhaust valves are open together. A crankcase compression type of engine cannot be used however, as the air must

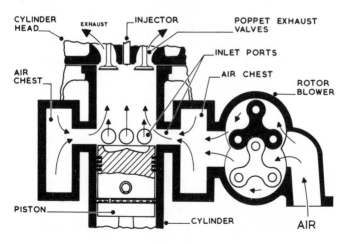

Fig. 5.8   Two-stroke C.I. engine

be compressed so highly; instead, the air is forced into the cylinders by an air blower or supercharger. The air pressures commonly employed are up to about 50 kN/m².

In one type of two-stroke C.I. engine the exhaust valves are of the poppet valve type operated by push rods. The piston itself acts as an inlet valve, closing off ports in the cylinder walls which communicate with an air chest charged by the blower. The blower generates pressure in the chest because it forces air into it faster than the engine can consume it. The blower may be an exhaust gas driven impeller, or a mechanically driven vane or rotor type.

Two-stroke cycle

At B.D.C. the piston sides are exposing the ports from the air chest and air is being blown into the cylinder to both charge the cylinder and expel the exhaust gases through the open exhaust valves. As the piston moves upward it closes the air ports at about the same time as the exhaust valves are closed. The air is then highly compressed by the piston and fuel is injected just before T.D.C.

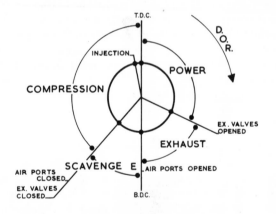

Fig. 5.9   Two-stroke timing

The fuel spray is broken up by, and mixed with, the air to start combustion. The expansion of the air forces the piston down the bore to provide the power stroke, and the exhaust valves are opened before the piston opens the air ports to restart the cycle.

6   The Cooling System

Function

As the petrol in the mixture is burned in the air inside the combustion chambers, a great deal of heat energy is released. Only about one-quarter of this heat energy is converted into mechanical energy so the remainder, or the excess heat, must be carried away from the metal parts forming the combustion chambers to prevent them being burned or expanded excessively. For a fraction of a second only, the temperature of the burning mixture is well above the melting point of both the iron and aluminium alloys used in the construction of the parts of the engine. The excess heat must therefore be removed quickly and continuously and this is the function of the cooling system.

Note that only one-quarter, approximately, of each litre of petrol supplies useful work, that is, the thermal efficiency of the petrol engine is only about 25%. The compression-ignition engine is a little better in its conversion of heat energy into mechanical energy, its thermal efficiency being about 40%.

Two main cooling systems are used in vehicle engines. The air-cooled systems use air as their cooling medium and water-cooled systems use air and water.

AIR COOLING

This type is used more frequently in motor-cycle and aircraft engines, although a few car engines are cooled by air. Some stationary engines are air cooled also, usually by means of a driven fan. Air cooling is not often used for multi-cylinder engines because it is difficult to cool all the cylinders equally, and the control of temperature is not very accurate. A rather complicated system of baffles is often needed and these are vulnerable to dirt and damage.

In air-cooled systems the cylinders and heads are heavily finned to increase the heat-dissipating areas. Aluminium alloys are used wherever possible because these are better heat conductors than irons and steels. Air-cooled engines run at higher temperatures than water-cooled engines so their bearing clearances must be larger. Due to the absence of sound-baffling water jackets they are usually more noisy in operation.

A simplified example of a controlled air-cooling system is shown in Fig. 6.2. The cylinders are enclosed by a sheet-metal housing through which the air flows. The inlet is varied in size by a shutter controlled, through a system of levers, by a thermostat fitted inside the housing. An engine-driven fan maintains the air flow under all conditions.

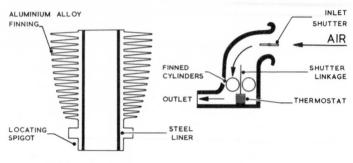

Fig. 6.1   Air cooling   Fig. 6.2   Controlled air cooling

WATER COOLING

Arrangement

The simple cooling system consists of the water jackets of the cylinder head and block, the radiator and two rubber pipes of large internal diameters. The pipes connect the highest point of the cylinder head to the top tank of the radiator, and the bottom tank of the radiator to the lowest point of the cylinder block (Fig. 6.3).

Operation

When the engine is running, the water in the cylinder head absorbs heat and expands. The same volume of heated water therefore weighs less than colder water and rises to the highest point of the system, passing out of the cylinder head and into the top tank of the radiator. Colder water from the radiator bottom tank moves in to take its place and so a slow circulation of the water is obtained by means of convection currents.

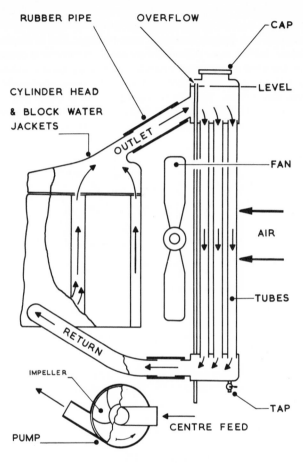

Fig. 6.3   Simple cooling system

As the heated water passes down through the tubes of the radiator most of its heat is extracted by the stream of air which passes around the tubes. By careful design the water temperature can be kept within the range of temperature at which the engine operates most efficiently and most economically.

The Radiator

Function

The radiator is designed to expose to the air stream as large a cooling area as possible in as small a frontal area as possible. It also acts as a tank for some of the water carried.

Construction

The usual form of construction is that of sheet-steel or brass pressings which are formed into top and bottom tanks. These are connected by

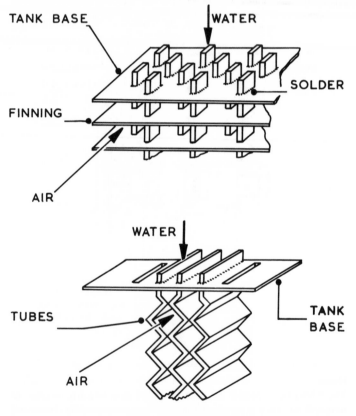

Fig. 6.4   (a) tubular; (b) film

brass or copper tubes fitted with finning to increase their surface areas. The block of tubes is sometimes termed the core, and in the radiators of cars and the lighter commercial vehicles the core may be of the tubular or of the film type.

Fan

The fan is used to draw air through the radiator when the vehicle is moving slowly or is stationary. It must be fairly close to the radiator core and it is usually driven by the same vee-belt as that used to drive the generator. In modern car engines the fan and the water pump are combined into a single unit mounted on the cylinder head.

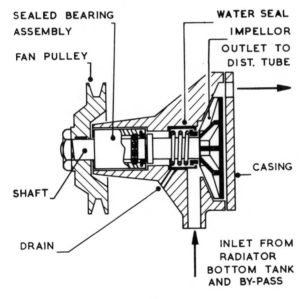

Fig. 6.5   Impeller pump

Hoses

The rubber hoses used in the cooling system must be fairly resistant to heat and oil. They must also be fairly strong mechanically. Hoses are usually moulded into their correct shape, and are either fabric reinforced or thick walled. Those used in pressurised cooling systems operating under higher pressures of between 48 and 100 kN/m^2 must have extra reinforcement.

It is important that hoses be examined at regular intervals and kept clean and in good condition. Dry and cracking hoses, and oil-soaked and spongy hoses, must be replaced.

Water pump (impeller)

Very large engines require large quantities of water to ensure adequate cooling and as a litre of water has a mass of 1 kg, the mass and volume of water needed could be excessive. This is avoided by the use of a water pump which circulates the water at increased speeds, i.e. a small volume and mass of water does as much cooling by forced circulation as a larger volume which is circulated by natural convection currents.

The pressurised system, Fig. 6.6

Construction

This is similar to that of the simpler system but a wider and lower radiator is used, and a thermostat, a water distributor tube and an engine-driven impeller pump are added. The pump circulates the water at a higher speed and much more positively than the convection currents of the simpler system, but a pressure is not built up by the pump. The thermostat is a temperature-controlled valve which is fitted into the water outlet from the cylinder head and which, by controlling the amount of cooling being done by the radiator, keeps the engine operating in its correct temperature range. The distributor tube is secured into the cylinder head and is perforated at certain points to direct the cooled water from the pump to the hottest parts of the cylinder head.

Operation

Engine hot. In this system the impeller pump draws cooled water from the bottom tank of the radiator and passes it into the distributor tube. The tube directs cooled water through its perforations on to the hottest areas of metal surrounding the combustion chambers and the exhaust ports. The cooled water absorbs most of the heat and passes up around the open valve of the thermostat and out of the cylinder head to the top tank of the radiator. As the heated water passes down the radiator core, the absorbed heat is removed by the air stream through the core, and the

now cooled water is drawn into the impeller pump to be recirculated.
Engine cold. The circulation starts as soon as the engine is started, so
the warming time would be unduly long if it were not for the action of
the thermostat. Under cold conditions, this valve is closed, and the
pump is only allowed to circulate the water in the cylinder head and

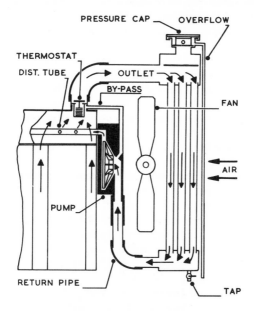

Fig. 6.6   Pressurised system

block. This is made possible by the use of a by-pass, either internal or
external, from the low-pressure side of the impeller to a point just below
the valve seat of the thermostat.

As the water absorbs heat its temperature rises, and at about 77 °C
the thermostat valve begins to open to allow water to pass into the
radiator and be cooled. This valve will open to positions related to the
air temperature, the vehicle speed, and the load on the engine. In this
manner the engine is kept within the temperature range at which it
operates best, and under cold conditions need have only the same
warm-up time as engines with the simple system.

The thermostat (bellows type), Fig. 6.7

Function

The thermostat is used to control the flow of water through the radiator. When the engine is cold it prevents water leaving the water jacket; when the engine is hot it allows water to pass from the water jacket and through the radiator at a rate sufficient to keep the water temperature within the 77 °C–85 °C range. In some vehicles a thermostat is used to regulate the flow of *air* through the radiator. This it does by controlling a valve in a pressurised oil system; this valve in turn, by means of piston and cylinder-operated levers, opens and closes a set of shutters in the front of the radiator.

Construction

The unit is composed of a disc valve and seat, and is fitted between the cylinder head and the radiator top tank. The valve is attached to the top of a stack of thin brass capsules arranged to form a bellows. These are filled with a volatile liquid such as acetone or methyl alcohol, and the bellows is secured to the frame and suspended from the seat.

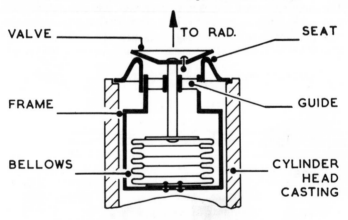

Fig. 6.7   Thermostat: bellows type

Operation

Engine cold. Under cold conditions, the valve is held closed down to its seat by the contraction of the bellows, and no water can pass from the cylinder head to the radiator.

Engine hot. As the water in the jacket is heated, the volatile liquid in the bellows is converted into a vapour. This causes each bellows to expand and the total expansion lifts the valve from its seat. The water can now flow from the cylinder head to be cooled in the radiator, that is, circulation is started. When the engine is switched off, the valve is pulled down to its seat by the contraction of the bellows, as the vaporised alcohol is converted into a liquid by the lower temperatures, until it is fully closed, when the temperature has fallen below 77 °C.

The pressure cap, Fig. 6.8

When an engine with impeller-assisted cooling system is worked hard there is a danger that pockets of steam may be formed in the complicated shape of the cylinder-head water jacket. Steam is a very poor conductor of heat and overheating may occur at these points. This will lead to pre-ignition and a loss of power, so this danger is reduced by using a special design of radiator neck and cap.

Construction

This cap has the usual seating in the tank neck, and also includes two extra valves which are opposed to each other. The larger spring-loaded valve prevents the release of pressure from the system until a pressure of 27 to 48 kN/m^2 is exceeded (in some systems pressures up to 100 kN/m^2

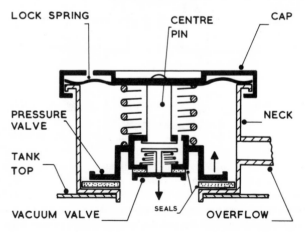

Fig. 6.8   Pressure cap: open valve type

are used). This means that the system normally operates under pressure and this prevents the water boiling and forming steam until the temperature is above the normal boiling-point. The engine may therefore be safely operated at a temperature higher than normal. It will also develop a little more power.

Operation

When the engine is running normally the excessive pressures, together with some steam or water, are released by the lifting of the large valve against the action of its spring. The water so released escapes down the overflow pipe.

As the engine is allowed to cool down after use the small losses result in the formation of a partial vacuum in the system. This is relieved by the opening of the smaller valve when the difference between the internal pressure and that of the outside atmosphere exceeds 7 kN/m². This allows air to enter the system through the overflow pipe, the valve being closed by its spring as the pressures equalise.

Advantages

The advantages of this system over the simple system are:

(a) The positive circulation is faster, so less mass and bulk of water are needed.

(b) A smaller and lighter radiator can be used, and its position in relation to the water jacket is not so limited.

(c) Smaller bore pipes may be used.

(d) The water level is not so critical because the circulation does not depend upon convection currents.

(e) Control of the engine-operating temperature is more accurate.

Although this system is more complicated and more expensive to produce and to maintain, its use is justified by greater efficiency and by more freedom for body designers and stylists.

A pressurised system is essential for vehicles which are to be operated at very high altitudes. At an altitude of about 7000 feet above sea level the boiling-point of water is about 95 °C; this is due to the fact that at this altitude the atmospheric pressure is reduced by about 20 kN/m². The losses of water under these conditions would be so great that the cooling system is suitably pressurised to prevent the formation of steam.

Note. The cap and the neck of the top tank are so designed that the pressure, when the engine is hot, may be released *before* the cap is completely free from the neck. This is done to reduce the possibility of boiling water being blown up into the face of the person removing the cap. The cap should only be part turned and then held until the hissing of the escaping pressure has ceased. The cap may then be released in safety.

System maintenance

Air cooled

The only regular work needed is the cleaning of the finning and the clearing and repairing of the ducting system. Where fans are used their drive-belt tension may need periodic adjustment.

Water cooled

The following points should be noted:

(a) Whenever possible use only soft water. In hard water districts, the use of an inhibitor such as potassium dichlorate will reduce the tendency of the limestone deposits in the water to combine with rust to form sludge.

(b) Check the water level at weekly intervals.

(c) Examine the rubber hoses and replace them if dry and cracked, or if oil-soaked and spongy. Check the tightness of the clips.

(d) Before installing anti-freeze: (i) check all joints and pipes and renew if necessary, (ii) back flush the system, including the heater, and (iii) mix the anti-freeze with some water, pour into the radiator, top up, and warm up the engine. Top up again when the engine is warm. Retain some of the mixture for subsequent topping-up during the winter.

(e) Check the thermostat and the pressure cap for their correct operation and renew if necessary.

Winter precautions

Water has its maximum density, i.e. its least volume for a given mass, at 4 °C. At temperatures above and below 4 °C its volume is greater. At about 0 °C ordinary water changes into ice and its volume increases. The forces due to this expansion act in all directions, and are large enough to fracture any metal parts holding or surrounding the water, e.g. the engine water jackets and the radiator. This possible damage may be avoided by either *completely* draining the system or by the use of an anti-freeze. The use of anti-freeze is preferable for cars and the smaller commercial vehicles as the interior heater cannot easily be drained, and it is seldom convenient to drain and refill. The cost of the greater quantities of anti-freeze needed for the larger vehicles may rule out its use for their systems, but where fleets are garaged it may be possible to heat the garages or have supplies of hot water available for filling the systems each morning.

In extremely cold weather, when anti-freeze is not used, the thermostat may be closed for a longer time than normal. Under these conditions the water in the bottom tank of the radiator may freeze and stop the circulation of the water before the thermostat opens. It is then possible to have boiling water in the top tank and ice in the bottom tank of the radiator at the same time, because water is a relatively poor conductor of heat. This possibility may be avoided by the use of a shield or muff to protect the bottom tank from the stream of very cold air.

Anti-freeze

Any impurity in water will raise its boiling point and lower its freezing point. The anti-freeze used in vehicle cooling systems is, in effect, an impurity which lowers its freezing point. It also inhibits against corrosion and may contain a colour dye to assist in the location of slight leaks. The most widely used anti-freeze is a mixture of glycerine and alcohol, or ethylene glycol, plus a corrosion inhibitor such as potassium dichromate.

Before anti-freeze is placed into the system the system should be back flushed to wash out all sludge and loose particles of rust and dirt. All hoses and clips should be checked for serviceability and replaced if necessary.

Anti-freeze should be mixed with water before being placed into the system, the usual quantities being in the ratio of one litre of anti-freeze to each four litres of water. This strength of mixture provides adequate protection for the usual British winter temperatures, a stronger mixture giving protection against lower temperatures. The strength of the mixture should be checked at regular intervals by the use of a special hydrometer, anti-freeze being added to bring the solution back to the correct strength.

If the system is frequently topped-up with water the diluted solution will permit the formation of small pieces of soft ice. These may lock the impeller of the pump and result in the fracture of its drive shaft, or may block the tubes of the radiator, both of which will result in the over-heating of the engine.

Muffs and blinds

In very cold conditions a radiator muff or blind may be used to assist in the more rapid warm-up of the engine, usually by shielding the lower part of the radiator from the stream of very cold air. Care must be taken to avoid overheating and it is advisable to use a water temperature gauge in conjunction with a spring-loaded blind.

Under very cold conditions the use of sump, and under-bonnet, heaters makes possible easy starting and a quicker engine warm-up. They ensure freedom from condensation and provide a small amount of heat.

The Transmission System

Speed and load

The petrol engine can only operate efficiently within a limited range of engine speeds, usually between 2000 and 4000 crankshaft revolutions per minute. The power produced by the engine is available at the crankshaft as a combination of speed and torque. This power will be capable of propelling the vehicle against a certain maximum load or resistance; any load in excess of this maximum will result in slowing down the engine. It will, therefore, produce less and less power until it is brought to a standstill or 'stalled'.

The loads imposed upon the engine will vary with the weight being moved and the nature of the road, i.e. level, uphill or downhill. The greatest amount of power is required when first moving the vehicle from rest.

As power is the speed multiplied by the torque ($P = S \times T$) it follows that if the speed is reduced the torque can be increased. By placing a train of gears between the crankshaft and the driving road wheels the turning power of the wheels can be increased by reducing their speed. This enables an engine of a given power output to overcome a greater load – but at a lower speed. In practice three or four alternative gear trains are used which give a choice of speeds and torques to suit all conditions of vehicle speed and engine loading.

A neutral position must be available to allow the running of the engine while the vehicle is stationary and a reversing gear train must also be available. All the various gear trains and their selector mechanisms are built into a gearbox which is fitted between the clutch and the final drive mechanism in the rear axle.

The sliding mesh three-speed gearbox

The simple three-speed and reverse sliding mesh gearbox is composed of an input shaft, a layshaft and an output shaft (see Fig. 7.1). The gears on the input and layshafts are integral with their shafts. The gears

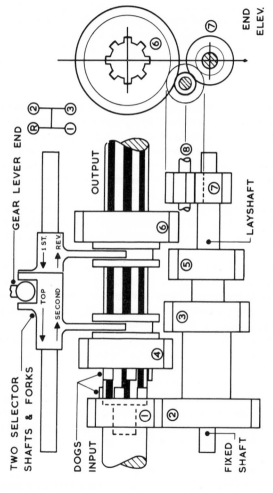

Fig. 7.1   Sliding mesh gearbox (three speed)

on the output shaft are splined so that they can be moved along their shaft but must always rotate with it. The input and output shafts are arranged on the same axis, or centre line, the forward end of the output shaft being supported in a bush or bearing inside the input shaft. Both shafts are supported and located by ball bearings in the end walls of the gearbox case. The layshaft is usually supported by needle roller bearings and located axially by phosphor-bronze thrust washers. The layshaft rotates upon a fixed shaft supported by the end walls of the gearbox case. A reverse idler gear (8) is permanently in mesh with the smallest of the layshaft gears (7) and is arranged to one side of the lay-shaft in such a way that the largest output gear (6) can connect with it when required.

Selector forks, which slide with their selector shafts, engage with grooves in the sliding output gears. Each is located by a spring-loaded ball or plunger, and a system of interlocking is arranged so that only one train at a time can be engaged. The selector shafts are moved by a gear lever which is pivoted on a ball joint in the lid of the box. This lever can be moved sideways as well as forwards and backwards to engage the desired train.

Operation, Fig. 7.2

Neutral. When neutral is selected the output gears are not meshed with any of the layshaft gears. The crankshaft torque, transmitted through the clutch, simply rotates the input shaft and the layshaft. No torque is transmitted to the output shaft, propeller shaft, and final drive mechanism and road wheels.

First (bottom) gear. The selector fork moves the rearmost output gear (6) along its shaft to engage with the third gear (5) of the layshaft. The crankshaft torque is now transmitted from the input gear (1) to the layshaft gear (2) and then from the layshaft gear (5) to the output gear (6) and from the output shaft to the final drive. Because of the different numbers of teeth between the gears this ratio provides the greatest torque increase and the greatest speed reduction, i.e. the lowest forward vehicle speed but the most powerful.

Second gear. The selector fork of the previous train is returned to its neutral position and the inner end of the gear lever engaged with the other selector shaft. This selector fork moves output gear (4) along its shaft to engage with the second layshaft gear (3). The torque is now transmitted from the layshaft through these gears to

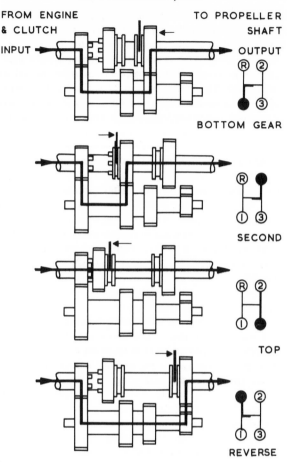

Fig. 7.2 Power paths of selected gears

the output shaft. The torque increase is less than that of the first gear train but the output speed is increased.

Third (top) gear. The selector fork is moved in the opposite direction from second gear to engage output gear (4) with the input gear (1) by means of *dogs*, or interlocking projections. This connects the two shafts and the output shaft is therefore driven directly at crankshaft speed and under the available crankshaft torque, i.e. in top gear there is no increase of torque over that of the crankshaft.

Reverse. The first gear selector shaft moves the output gear (6) to engage with the reverse idler gear (8). The torque is transmitted from the input gear (1) to the layshaft gear (2) and then from layshaft (7) to idler (8) and from idler (8) to output (6) and to the output shaft. This provides a reversal of the direction of drive. Often the speed reduction and torque increase in this gear are the largest in the gearbox.

The gear case is usually a cast iron or aluminium alloy casting holding between 0·5 and 1 litre of lubricating oil. Oil seals are required to avoid wastage through the bearings in the gearbox walls and these take the form of spring-loaded leather or plastic units and paper gaskets.

The sliding mesh four-speed gearbox

In construction and arrangement this gearbox is generally similar to the three-speed type but there are a few important differences. These are:

(1) The incorporation of an extra gear train makes available an extra series of intermediate torques, which enables the engine to overcome the loads acting against it without either being overworked or having to operate at excessive speeds.

(2) The reverse idler gear has two sets of teeth, of different diameter, and is engaged by being moved bodily along its own shaft; i.e. it is not permanently engaged with the layshaft.

(3) The reverse idler gear has its own selector shaft and fork, and the gear lever has five different positions. The reverse gear selector mechanism is so arranged that reverse cannot be selected by accident. This is usually accomplished by having to use extra force, or an unusual lifting or side movement of the gear lever.

Construction, Fig. 7.3

The input and output shafts lie on the same axis and, although the forward end of the output shaft is supported in a bush fitted inside the input shaft, there is no direct connection between them. These shafts are supported and located by ball bearings mounted in the end walls of the gearbox case.

The layshaft axis is parallel with the other two shafts and lies under or to one side of them, the largest layshaft gear wheel, or *pinion*, being permanently engaged with the integral pinion of the input shaft. The

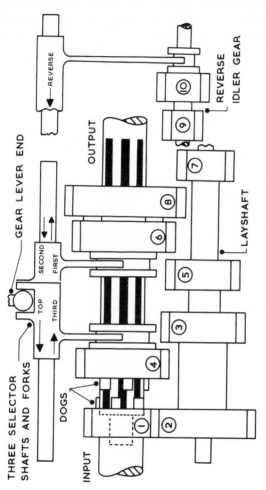

Fig. 7.3 Four-speed sliding mesh

layshaft rotates upon plain bushes or needle-roller bearings which are supported by a non-rotating shaft. End-float is controlled by phosphor-bronze spacer washers.

The layshaft has four integral pinions which have spur teeth. The output shaft is splined and carries splined pinions which provide the third-, second-, and first-gear ratios. The movement of the gear lever, acting through the selector shafts and forks, causes the selected pinion to slide along the output shaft and be meshed with one of the layshaft pinions.

Operation, Figs. 7.3 and 7.4

First or bottom gear. The selector fork moves the double-output pinion (6 and 8) to the rear to engage (8) with the rear layshaft pinion (7). The torque is transmitted through input (1) to layshaft pinion (2), then layshaft pinion (7) to output pinion (8). This ratio provides the greatest forward speed reduction and torque increase.

Second gear. The selector fork moves the double-output pinion (6 and 8) forward to engage pinion (6) with the third layshaft gear (5). The torque is transmitted through input (1) to layshaft pinion (2), then layshaft pinion (5) to output pinion (6). This ratio provides more speed but less torque increase than that of the first gear.

Third gear. The selector fork of the third- and top-gear selector-shaft moves the output pinion (4) to the rear to engage with the second layshaft pinion (3). The torque is transmitted through input (1) to layshaft (2) and from layshaft (3) to output (4). This ratio provides more speed but less torque increase than the first- and second-gear ratios.

Top gear. The selector fork moves the output pinion (4) forward to engage with input pinion (1) by means of dogs. The input and output shafts now rotate as one shaft, and the output speed and torque are the same as that of the crankshaft.

N.B. Note that bottom gear provides the greatest forward speed reduction and the greatest torque increase. As the other ratios are engaged the output speed is increased while the output torque is reduced until, when top gear is engaged, the input and output speeds and torques are the same as those of the crankshaft.

Reverse gear, Fig. 7.5. The output pinions remain in the neutral position, that is (4) between layshaft (2 and 3), and (6 and 8) between layshaft (5 and 7). The reverse selector shaft and fork move the double reverse

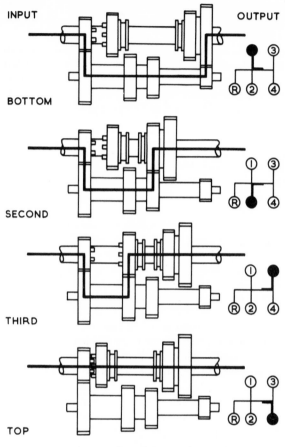

Fig. 7.4   Power paths

idler pinion (9 and 10) to engage with layshaft (7) and output (8) at the same time (see Fig. 7.6). The torque is now transmitted through input (1) to layshaft (2) and from layshaft (7) to reverse idler (10). Then from reverse idler (9) to output (8). In many gearboxes the reverse ratio provides the greatest reduction in speed and the greatest increase in torque.

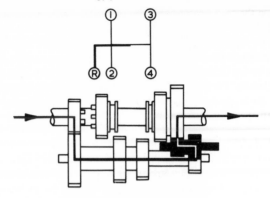

Fig. 7.5   Reverse power path

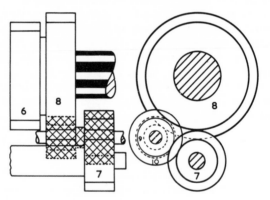

IDLER IO ENGAGED WITH LAYSHAFT 7
IDLER 9   ENGAGED WITH OUTPUT 8

Fig. 7.6   Idler engaged

Synchronisation

Even when the clutch is used to interrupt the transmission of torque to the driving pinion, it is very difficult to slide another pinion into mesh with it unless they are both rotating at about the same speed. If the speeds are not the same (i.e. synchronised) the teeth will clash and cause damage to each other or fail to engage.

When the engagement of a particular ratio is required, it is essential that the speed of rotation of the layshaft pinion involved in the train is about the same as that of the pinion on the output shaft. Note that when the vehicle is in motion, and the clutch is released, the output pinions are driven by the propeller shaft. When changing up, therefore, the speed of the layshaft (and that of the engine) must be reduced. When changing down, the layshaft and engine speed must be increased. These changes of layshaft speed are obtained by 'double declutching'.

Double declutching
When changing up the clutch is released, the gear lever moved into the neutral position, and the accelerator pedal eased back. The clutch is then re-engaged and the layshaft speed reduced by the now slower-running engine. The clutch is then momentarily released, the required gear engaged with the layshaft, and the clutch re-engaged.

When changing down the clutch is released, the gear lever moved into neutral, and the clutch re-engaged. The engine is then accelerated to increase the speed of the layshaft. The clutch is then momentarily released, the required gear engaged with the layshaft, and the clutch re-engaged.

This sequence of operations demands a fair degree of skill and judgement on the part of the driver if clean and silent gear changes are to be obtained. A great deal of time and money has been spent in developing ratio change mechanisms which reduce the skill and judgement needed and these have resulted in the synchromesh gearboxes, and in the semi-automatic and fully automatic changing gearboxes.

A development of the sliding pinion, or sliding mesh, gearbox was used for a number of years. This was known as the constant mesh, sliding dog, gearbox.

The constant mesh gearbox, Fig. 7.7
This is an improvement of the sliding mesh type. The layout of the pinions (and the general arrangement of the box) is very similar to that previously described. The output pinions, however, are constantly in mesh with those of the layshaft and rotate on splined bushes independent of the output shaft.

When a particular gear ratio is required, the output pinion involved is locked to the output shaft by means of a dog clutch. This is moved along the shaft by its selector fork instead of the pinion being moved.

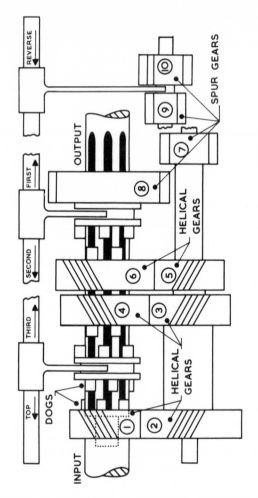

Fig. 7.7   Four-speed constant mesh gearbox

In this way the pinion teeth are prevented from clashing, and so being damaged, but this liability is transferred to the teeth of the dog clutches. These must still be synchronised with the pinions before the engagement can be made and double declutching is still required. In spite of this it is easier to make a clean and silent change with this gearbox than with the sliding mesh type.

THE CLUTCH

Function

The main function of the clutch is to interrupt the transmission of crankshaft torque to the gearbox. Different trains of gears, providing different combinations of speed and torque, must be used to suit different driving and load conditions but it is almost impossible to engage, or release, gears when they are transmitting torque. It is also practically impossible to engage a rotating gear, under torque, with a stationary or slower-running gear – and it certainly cannot be done without damage.

The clutch is also designed to absorb the shock of engaging two shafts running at different speeds, and to absorb small torque irregularities.

Types

The most widely used form of clutch is the friction type. This may be:
(a) the cone clutch which is now only used in the synchromesh units of gearboxes, and in overdrives and some epicyclic gearboxes;
(b) the single-plate clutch (multi spring or diaphragm spring) which is used in most cars and small commercial vehicles;
(c) the multi-plate clutch which is used in motor-cycles and in some racing cars and tractors, and also in special types of very heavy commercial and civil engineering vehicles.

The single- and multi-plate friction clutches are usually dry types but some wet types are still in use. In these cork-insert or phosphor-bronze plates are fitted between steel plates, all the plates being immersed in oil.

Other forms of clutch are coming into wider use and generally form a part of the pre-selector, two-pedal, or fully automatic transmission systems. These are the centrifugal and magnetic clutches, the fluid flywheel, and the hydraulic torque converter.

Single-plate multi-spring clutch

Construction

The single-plate clutch (Fig. 7.8) consists of a centre plate which is clamped between two other plates. These two outer plates are driven by the engine crankshaft, and in turn drive the centre plate which is mounted upon the splined gearbox input shaft. The rear face of the

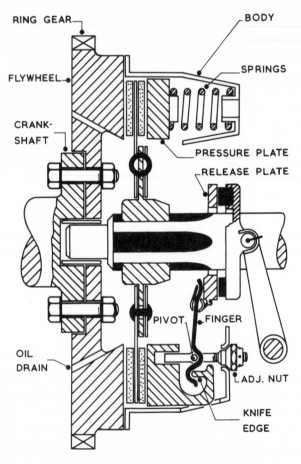

Fig. 7.8   Single-plate clutch (multi spring)

flywheel is used as one driving plate and the second, or pressure, plate is mounted inside the clutch body which is bolted to the flywheel. The pressure plate is forced towards the flywheel by a set of strong springs which are arranged radially inside the body. Three levers, or fingers, are carried on pivots suspended from the case of the body, and are so arranged as to be able to prise the pressure plate away from the flywheel by the inward movement of a carbon or ball thrust-release bearing. The bearing is mounted upon a forked shaft and is moved forward by the depression of the clutch pedal. The connection between the pedal and the shaft may be made by means of rods, cables, chain, or by an hydraulic system.

The hub of the centre plate is free to move along the splines of the gearbox input shaft, and carries a disc to which are riveted friction linings of an asbestos material. The disc is only connected to its hub through a set of strong and radially arranged springs. The linings are made to flex or separate slightly when not under load. This is obtained by the offsetting or crimping of the segmented outer edge of the disc, and is done to reduce the tendency of the linings to stick to the driving plates during release. It also helps in obtaining a smoother take-up of torque at the beginning of the re-engagement action.

Operation

Release. When the clutch pedal is depressed its linkage forces the thrust-release bearing to move in towards the flywheel, pressing the longer ends of the fingers inward. The fingers are forced to turn on their suspended pivot and so prise the pressure plate away from the flywheel by the knife-edges, at the same time compressing the clutch springs. This action removes the pressure from the centre plate and, by reducing the friction between the driving and driven plates, releases the gearbox input shaft from the crankshaft torque.

Engagement. When the fresh gear train has been engaged the clutch pedal is steadily released. The fingers now move out and allow the springs to extend and force the pressure plate back towards the flywheel. As this happens the friction linings on the centre plate disc are gripped between the driving plates and, as the friction increases, are forced to rotate at a speed different from that of the hub and the gearbox input shaft. The centre plate radial springs are therefore compressed and so cushion the shock of the initial torque take-up. As the input shaft and the crankshaft match speeds the radial springs extend and the engine torque is transmitted through them to the gearbox. Small torque irregularities are also absorbed by these springs being slightly compressed and released during normal running.

It is important that there should be about 19 mm of free pedal movement. This allows the release bearing to move about 1·5 mm away from the fingers and so prevents clutch slip being caused externally.

Single-plate diaphragm-spring clutch

Construction

In these clutches a steel diaphragm spring is used to force the pressure

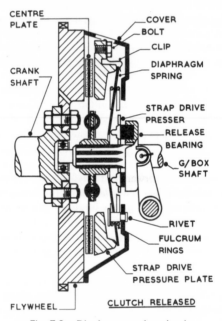

Fig. 7.9   Diaphragm spring clutch

plate towards the flywheel. This spring is a saucer-shaped disc, of hardened and tempered steel, which has radially arranged slots cut from the hollow centre towards the outer edge. Shouldered rivets, which pass through elongated holes at the outer ends of the slots, secure the diaphragm to the clutch cover. These rivets also hold in position the fulcrum rings on which the diaphragm pivots. These rings are of circular cross-section and one ring is fitted at each side of the diaphragm. The outer edge of the diaphragm is located on the pressure plate by a series of bolted clips, and the pressure plate is driven by straps. The presser plate of the thrust-release bearing abuts the centre of the diaphragm spring and is secured to the cover by three tangentially arranged flexible steel straps. The centre plate is of the flexible, or spring-drive, type.

Operation

When the clutch assembly is bolted to the flywheel, the diaphragm spring is flattened and exerts a powerful thrust on the pressure plate – so trapping the centre plate firmly between it and the flywheel. When the clutch is disengaged, the centre of the diaphragm is forced inwards. The diaphragm pivots between the fulcrum rings and its outer edge (acting through the clips), withdraws the pressure plate, and releases the centre plate.

ALTERNATIVE ARRANGEMENTS OF TRANSMISSION ASSEMBLIES

The arrangement of the power and transmission units of the conventional car and commercial vehicle are very similar (see Figs. 1.5 and 1.8). The engine, clutch and gearbox are bolted together to form a single unit which is mounted in the forward end of the chassis. The final drive gear assembly is mounted in the rear axle, and is driven by a long propeller shaft which may be made in two parts if the chassis is a long wheelbase type.

This basic arrangement may also be used in conjunction with independent rear suspension, the final drive gearing being secured to the rear of the chassis and the wheels driven by two short shafts. An example of this arrangement is that of the Triumph Herald. Other arrangements of the transmission system are possible and to a large extent these depend upon the position of the engine in the chassis.

Where the engine is forward mounted and the front wheels are each driven by a short shaft, the clutch, gearbox and final drive gear assembly are all forward mounted with the engine. The relative positions of these units vary between manufacturers but the path taken by the driving torque is exactly the same as in the conventional arrangement. In the Citroën the gearbox and final drive gear assembly are arranged forward of the engine. In the B.M.C. Mini Minor the engine is mounted across the chassis, and the gearbox and final drive are fitted into the engine sump (Fig. 7.10).

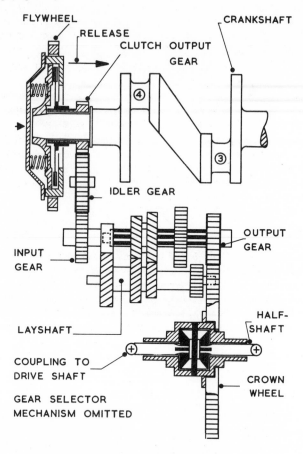

Fig. 7.10   Unit power plant

The Volkswagen engine is a horizontally opposed, four-cylinder air-cooled type which is mounted in the rear of the vehicle and drives the rear road wheels (Fig. 7.11). The clutch, final drive and gearbox are arranged in that order and are bolted to the forward end of the engine.

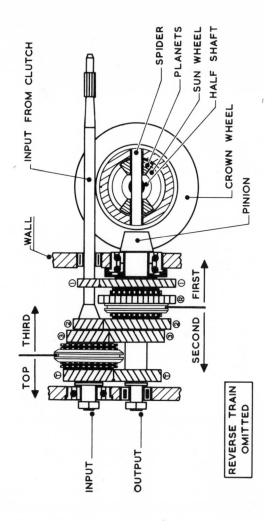

Fig. 7.11   Volkswagen drive

Although the final drive is fitted between the clutch and the gearbox, the crankshaft torque is transmitted through the gearbox to the final drive in the usual manner.

The engine of the Hillman Imp is an inclined four-cylinder, inline water-cooled design which is also mounted in the rear of the vehicle and drives the rear wheels. Like the Volkswagen, the final drive is arranged between the clutch and the gearbox but the crankshaft torque passes through the gearbox before passing through the final drive. Both are bolted to the forward end of the engine. The gearbox input shaft passes through the final drive gear assembly case while the output shaft is integral with the final drive pinion.

THE PROPELLER SHAFT

Function

The propeller shaft (Fig. 7.12) is used to connect the output shaft of the gearbox to the pinion shaft of the final drive mechanism in the rear axle. As the suspension system operates, the rear axle rises and falls continuously (see Fig. 7.13). It also moves backwards and forwards as it rises and falls in an arc, having as its centre the forward shackle pin of the rear spring. In addition, the pinion nose itself is forced upward when the engine torque is applied to the pinion, and is forced down when the brakes are applied. The propeller shaft must be so designed as to transmit the torque from the gearbox to the final drive smoothly and continuously in spite of all these different movements.

Arrangement

The propeller shaft is a tubular steel unit with a Hooke joint at each end. The joints consist of two U-shaped steel forgings or 'yokes' which are connected at 90° to each other by a four-legged cross or 'spider'. Needle roller or rubber bearings may be used to support the spider legs in the forgings. These U-joints, or universal joints, allow the smooth transmission of torque even though the gearbox and pinion shafts are never in exact alignment.

Velocity

When cross and ring joints are used to connect two shafts the driven shaft does not rotate with uniform velocity; i.e. it does not turn at the same speed during each part of a revolution. In one revolution the

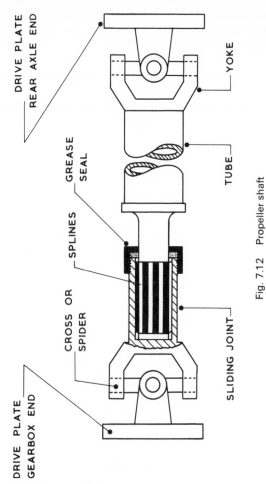

DRIVE PLATE
REAR AXLE END

YOKE

GREASE
SEAL

SPLINES

TUBE

CROSS OR
SPIDER

SLIDING JOINT

DRIVE PLATE
GEARBOX END

Fig. 7.12 Propeller shaft

driven shaft is accelerated twice and decelerated twice, this effect being increased as the angularity is increased. These velocity differences can be cancelled in the propeller shaft by the use of two correctly aligned joints, the acceleration of one being neutralised by the deceleration of the second. A single joint can safely be used if the angularity is small.

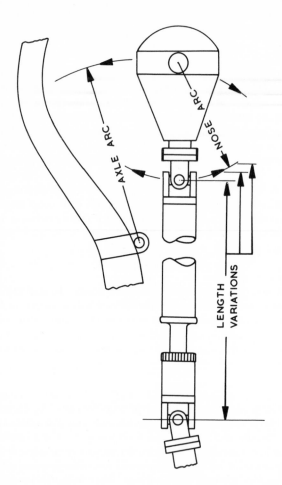

Fig. 7.13   Propeller shaft action

A sliding joint is used to allow the propeller shaft to change its length, as it rotates, to compensate for the small backward-and-forward movement of the rear axle caused by the action of the suspension system. It is simply a splined tubular portion built on to the forward universal joint, and it slides on splines on the propeller shaft, as shown in Fig. 7.12.

Critical speed

Every rotating shaft has one or more speeds at which it will 'whip'. This occurs when centrifugal force, acting at the centre of the length of the shaft, causes the shaft to bend. The speeds at which the centrifugal force becomes strong enough to do this are called *critical speeds*. By using a tube of large diameter, or of relatively thick wall, whip can be made to occur only at speeds above or below those normal for the shaft. Some shafts may be fitted with centre bearings and some may be counter-balanced.

Note. A hollow shaft is stronger than a solid shaft of the *same mass*. This is because the material at the centre of a solid shaft under torque loading is subjected only to small shear stresses. This material can be omitted without reducing the strength of the shaft although it does reduce its mass and cost.

The sliding joint, Fig. 7.14

As the rear springs are deflected by the road wheels, the rear axle is made to swing in an arc which has the forward spring shackle as its centre. The distance between the end of the gearbox output shaft and the pinion nose is therefore always altering. The sliding joint is fitted to the forward end of the propeller shaft and, in effect, allows the shaft to alter its effective length without interfering with the transmission of torque.

The sliding joint consists of a steel sleeve which is internally splined and is fitted over a splined extension of the propeller shaft. The sleeve is usually welded to one yoke or fork of the universal joint. The splines are protected from dirt and water by a cork oil seal secured by a knurled and circular nut. A grease nipple is fitted into the side of the sleeve.

In one arrangement the sliding joint forms a part of the propeller shaft assembly, each of the shaft driving flanges being bolted to a similar flange splined and locked to the gearbox output shaft and the pinion shaft respectively.

In another arrangement the sleeve portion is fitted forward of the

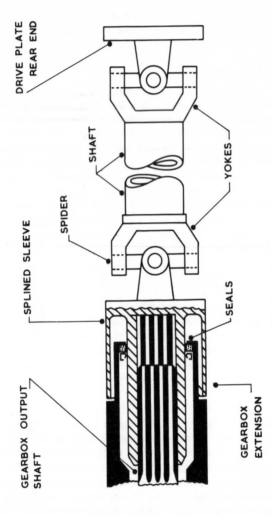

Fig. 7.14   Modern sliding joint

upper universal joint and moves on the gearbox output shaft. In this arrangement the propeller shaft can be completely removed by uncoupling the pinion end flange and withdrawing the shaft from the gearbox shaft and sleeve.

Universal joints

These are used to connect two shafts when their centre lines intersect.

Types of universal joints

The three main types of universal joint used in vehicle construction are:
(1) the cross type such as the 'Hardy-Spicer';
(2) the ring type such as the 'Layrub';
(3) the constant velocity types such as the 'Tracta' and the 'Rzeppa' joints.

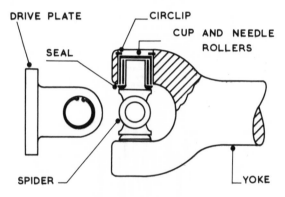

Fig. 7.15   Cross joint

Hardy-Spicer, Fig. 7.15

This consists of a four-legged cross, the ends of which are fitted into two opposed U-shaped yokes secured to the shafts. The ends of the cross are hardened and tempered, and turn on needle-roller bearings carried in hardened and tempered steel cups. These cups are fitted into the yokes and are retained by circlips. A seal is fitted at the inner side of each leg of the cross to retain oil or grease and to exclude water and dirt. These joints may be pre-packed with grease or oil, or they may be fitted with grease nipples.

This type of joint has a long service life and can operate efficiently with large differences of alignment between the axes of the shafts; i.e. with a large amount of shaft angularity.

Note. It is very important to ensure that when these joints are used in pairs they are correctly aligned in relation to each other. Failure to arrange the outer yokes in the same plane will destroy the balance of the shaft.

Layrub, Fig. 7.16

This consists of two steel pressings which are riveted together and support four or six steel bushes. Each bush is mounted in rubber and has a locating spigot which fits into a recess in the forked end of each shaft. The rubber used smooths out vibration and small torque irregularities, and will permit up to 13 mm of longitudinal movement. If two of these joints are employed a sliding joint may be omitted. This type requires little or no servicing and will operate efficiently with up to 15° of angularity.

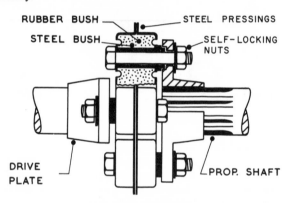

Fig. 7.16   Ring joint

Constant velocity joint

The joints previously described suffer from the disadvantage that the driven shaft will not rotate at the same velocity as the driving shaft, the driven shaft having two periods during each revolution in which it rotates faster than the driving shaft and two periods in which it rotates slower.

In the propeller shaft this disadvantage is overcome by the use of two Hooke's type joints which are so aligned to each other that the velocity increase of the one is neutralised by the velocity reduction of the other. Where space is limited, and where the angles between the shafts are relatively large, two joints cannot be used and a special joint of the constant velocity type has to be built into the transmission, e.g. front-wheel drive.

In these joints a mechanism is incorporated between the yokes which automatically aligns itself with the plane bisecting the angle formed by the two shafts. The alignment may be obtained through the movement of steel balls in grooves, or through the deflection of rubber components – these deflections neutralising the velocity variations.

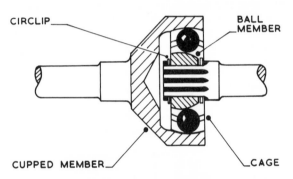

Fig. 7.17   Constant velocity joint

A commonly used constant velocity joint resembles a Hooke's or cross joint but the spider arms are mounted in split rubber bushes retained by steel shells and U-bolts. This type also has the advantages of permitting the use of large angles between the shafts, and reducing the transmission of shock loads and vibration.

8 The Final Drive

This is generally referred to as the *differential* but includes the crown wheel and pinion or other gear assembly having the same functions.

Functions

The crown wheel and pinion assembly is used
(a) to change the direction of the drive through a right angle, and
(b) to increase the available torque by reducing the speed (power = torque × speed). The ratios used in cars are about 4:1 while those of commercial vehicles may be as high as 10:1.

The differential is a second gear assembly which is bolted to the side of the crown wheel, or inside a worm-wheel, and which rotates with it. This unit allows the half-shafts to rotate at *different speeds* but under the *same torque*, and only comes into operation when the vehicle is cornering. Its function or purpose is to reduce the tendency for the tyres to be dragged sideways instead of rolling around the curved path. It also reduces the stresses imposed upon the shafts and bearings and reduces tyre wear. Skidding is also much less liable to occur.

Construction

Crown wheel and pinion

These are hardened and tempered steel bevel gears which are arranged with their axes at right angles. The larger is the crown wheel and this carries the differential assembly. The pinion is the smaller and is integral with a short shaft to which is bolted the propeller shaft. The complete final drive gear assembly is mounted in a strong steel casting which is bolted into the rear axle case. A tubular part of the casting, called the pinion nose, supports the pinion and its integral shaft either in double-thrust ball bearings or in opposed taper-roller bearings. Some designs may use a plain roller bearing at the inner end of the pinion. The differential case is formed into two arms which carry the bearings used to support and locate the crown wheel. These bearings may be either ball or taper-roller types and their thrust directions are opposed. Provision is made to adjust the meshing of the gears either by screwed sleeves, shims, or by pre-loading jigs and shims.

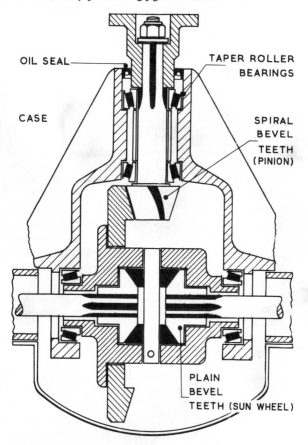

OIL SEAL

TAPER ROLLER BEARINGS

CASE

SPIRAL BEVEL TEETH (PINION)

PLAIN BEVEL TEETH (SUN WHEEL)

Fig. 8.1 Rear axle gearing mounted in casing

Differential, Fig. 8.2
This consists of a case (which may be in two parts) which is bolted or

riveted to the inner side of the crown wheel and rotates with it. Two or four planet wheels are mounted upon a spider shaft and are fitted inside the case in such a way that the spider shaft is turned end over end. Also

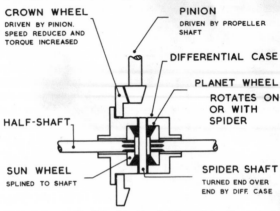

CROWN WHEEL
DRIVEN BY PINION.
SPEED REDUCED AND
TORQUE INCREASED

PINION
DRIVEN BY PROPELLER
SHAFT

DIFFERENTIAL CASE

PLANET WHEEL
ROTATES ON
OR WITH
SPIDER

HALF-SHAFT

SUN WHEEL
SPLINED TO SHAFT

SPIDER SHAFT
TURNED END OVER
END BY DIFF. CASE

Fig. 8.2   Layout of differential

fitted inside the case, and meshing with the plane wheels, are two sun wheels which are internally splined and which support and drive the inner ends of the half-shafts. The gear teeth and the spider shaft are the most highly stressed parts of the assembly and are those most liable to fracture.

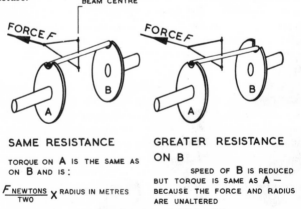

BEAM CENTRE

FORCE F

FORCE F

B

A

B

A

SAME RESISTANCE

TORQUE ON **A** IS THE SAME AS
ON **B** AND IS :

$\frac{F \text{ NEWTONS}}{\text{TWO}} \times \text{RADIUS IN METRES}$

GREATER RESISTANCE
ON **B**

SPEED OF **B** IS REDUCED
BUT TORQUE IS SAME AS **A** —
BECAUSE THE FORCE AND RADIUS
ARE UNALTERED

Fig. 8.3   Principle of differential

Differential principle, Fig. 8.3

This is similar to that of the simple bar type of brake compensator. In Fig 8.3 the ends of the beam are fitted into slots in the circumference of the discs. If a force is applied to the centre of the beam and at a tangent to the discs (at right angles to their radii), and if each disc offers the *same resistance* to being turned, then the reaction forces acting on each disc will be the same. The beam will not pivot about its centre, the discs will rotate at the same speeds, and the two torques or turning moments will be the same. In the practical differential the discs are the sun wheels on the half-shafts and the beam is the spider shaft and its planet wheels.

When one disc does offer more resistance to being turned than the other, the beam is forced to pivot about its centre. The disc with the greatest resistance will hold back while the other is pushed forward by the pivoting of the beam. Under the action of a continuous tangential force at the centre of the beam one disc is slower and one faster in rotation than the tangential force; i.e. the revolutions per minute lost by the disc with the greater resistance are gained by the other. The reaction forces on the discs are the same because the force available is divided equally by the beam. The radii are the same so the torque acting on each is the same (torque = force × radius) – although their speeds are now different.

Operation

Vehicle running straight, Fig. 8.4. The driving torque of the propeller shaft and of the pinion is increased by the speed reduction between the pinion and the crown wheel. The direction of the drive is turned bodily through a right angle.

The differential spider is rotated end over end, carrying the planet wheels with it although they do not rotate on the spider. The road wheels, half-shafts and sun wheels offer the same resistance to being turned and the differential gearing does not therefore operate.

Vehicle cornering, Fig. 8.5. During a turn the outer wheel has to move along an arc of greater radius than the inner wheel, and to do this in the same time it must be speeded up. The inner wheel is slowed down as the vehicle turns and this increases the resistance of its sun wheel. The spider shaft is still being turned end over end at crown wheel speed, and as the inner sun wheel slows the planet wheels are forced to rotate *on the spider shaft* and about the inner sun wheel. In so doing the speed of the outer sun, and the outer road wheel, is increased by the same proportion

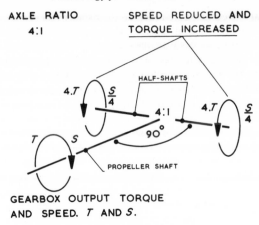

Fig. 8.4   Action of differential: running straight

as the speed of the inner sun is reduced. The torque is still divided equally between the two half-shafts but their speeds are different.

Note. The differential system only operates when there is a difference between the resistance to turning of the road wheels. When one wheel loses its grip on a poor surface its resistance is reduced to zero. The

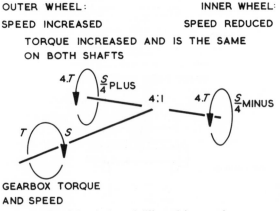

Fig. 8.5   Action of differential: cornering

planet gear wheels therefore rotate on their spider and run around the sun of the opposite wheel. This remains stationary and the slipping wheel is driven by *all* the available torque.

Vehicles which have to operate over poor ground (e.g. tractors, civil engineering and military vehicles) are often fitted with a device which puts the differential gearing out of operation as required. In effect the two half-shafts are joined together so that one wheel can drive when the other slips.

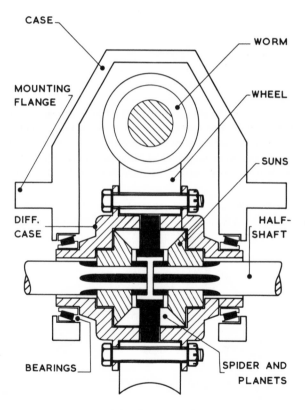

Fig. 8.6   Worm final drive

Oil sealing

In all the various designs of rear axle the axle case also acts as a tank for
the lubricating oil. The axle ends and the wheel hubs must be sealed to
prevent oil losses and this is usually accomplished by means of paper
gaskets and spring-loaded oil seals of leather, plastic, or oil-resistant
rubber. The joint face between the final drive assembly and the axle case
is also sealed by a paper gasket or a gasket of tougher material. The axle
case must also be vented to the atmosphere to prevent any build up of
pressure during operation. The venting often consists of a small hole
drilled in the top of the case near the U-bolt on the off-side.

Types of final drive

Cars and the lighter commercial vehicles use one of two main types of
crown wheel and pinion. These differ in the relationship between the
axis of the pinion and that of the crown wheel. As a result of this
difference they also differ in the shape of the gear teeth, the form of
frictional contact and in the type of lubricant required.

The heavier vehicles, which need a larger torque increase and a greater
reduction in speed, may use a worm and wheel in place of the crown
wheel and pinion (see Fig. 8.6). In some heavy vehicles a crown wheel
and pinion may be combined with various arrangements of helical or
bevel gears to produce double-reduction single- and two-speed axles.

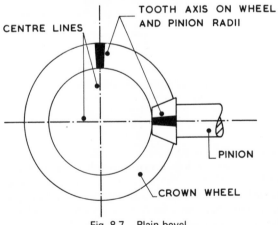

Fig. 8.7   Plain bevel

Whatever form of gearing is used to increase torque, the differential gear train is always fitted.

Plain bevel, Fig. 8.7
This is an early design which is no longer used. The axis of the pinion, when produced, passed through the centre of the crown wheel. Straight radial teeth were used but these proved to be weak, noisy and to wear rapidly.

Spiral bevel, Fig. 8.8
These were an improvement of the plain bevel and are still in use. The pinion axis produced passes through the centre of the crown wheel but the teeth are curved as well as radially arranged. The resulting increase in the length of the tooth increases strength and provides quieter running and a longer life in service.

In both these designs the teeth make a rolling contact.

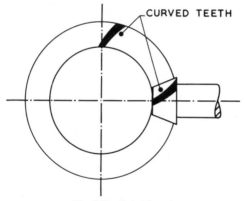

Fig. 8.8   Spiral bevel

Hypoid spiral bevel, Fig. 8.9
This is a common modern design in which the axis of the pinion produced passes above or below the centre of the crown wheel. This permits the body designer to produce either (a) a body having a normal ground clearance but with a flat floor, or (b) a body which retains the propeller shaft tunnel but has much less ground clearance. In the latter

the pinion axis is below the crown wheel centre, and the weight of the heavy unit is brought nearer to the ground – so helping to improve the road-holding qualities of the vehicle by bringing its centre of gravity nearer to the ground.

The teeth are curved and radially arranged but are of a different shape from that of the spiral bevel teeth. They are both longer and stronger and so have a longer service life. The hypoid type is slightly

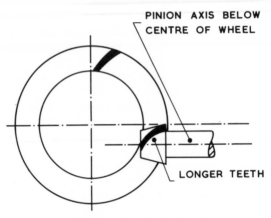

Fig. 8.9   Hypoid spiral bevel

more noisy in operation than the spiral bevel but this is usually reduced by the fitting of rubber types of spring bushes and by the use of thick rubber pads between the rear springs and the axle bed-plates.

The tooth contact is a combination of rolling and sliding friction which produces very high contact pressures. It is most important that only the correct grade of extreme-pressure hypoid oil be used.

Note. Crown wheels and pinions are mated together as a pair and must always be replaced as a pair and their correct mesh obtained.

Forces acting, Fig. 8.10
When gears are operating under load they always tend to move either closer to each other or farther away, that is into or out of mesh, depending upon the type of gear and the torques involved.

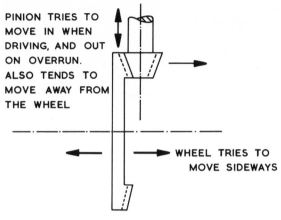

PINION TRIES TO MOVE IN WHEN DRIVING, AND OUT ON OVERRUN. ALSO TENDS TO MOVE AWAY FROM THE WHEEL

WHEEL TRIES TO MOVE SIDEWAYS

Fig. 8.10   Forces acting

On drive

When the pinion is driving the crown wheel against resistance the pinion tries to move sideways away from the wheel and, because of the curved shape of the teeth, also tries to move closer into mesh with the wheel. The wheel itself tries to move bodily away from the pinion.

On overrun

When the pinion is being driven by the crown wheel the pinion tries to move away from the wheel both sideways and along its axis. The crown wheel tries to move bodily closer to the pinion.

All of these movements must be controlled and limited by the types of bearing used. The crown wheel is carried between opposed ball or taper-roller thrust bearings which both support and locate the assembly; i.e. the bearings take the radial load and the thrust load in one direction. The pinion may be carried in two opposed thrust taper-roller bearings with a spacer between them, or it may be carried between a plain ball bearing, fitted at the inner end, and two opposed thrust ball bearings at the outer end.

Axle shafts

Three main methods are used to support the half-shafts in the rear axle case. In all of them the inner ends of the shafts are splined into, and

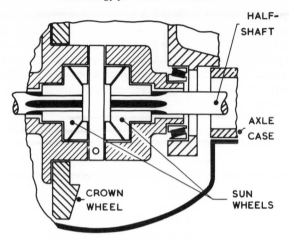

Fig. 8.11   Inner end support

supported by, the sun wheels of the differential assembly (see Fig. 8.11). The differences lie in the arrangement of the hub bearings in relation to both the case and the shaft, and in the forces or loads imposed upon the shaft itself.

Semi-floating, Fig 8.12
The hub and the half-shaft are, in effect, a one-piece unit although they

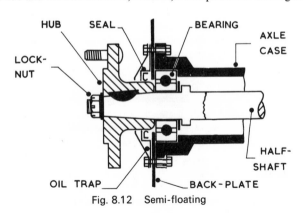

Fig. 8.12   Semi-floating

may in fact be splined or fitted together by means of a taper, key and lock-nut. The bearing is carried *on the shaft* and is located by a nut or a sleeve. The outer track of the bearing is fitted into a recess *in the axle case* and is located by a retainer plate bolted to the end flange of the axle case. This retainer usually encloses a spring-loaded oil seal and often incorporates an oil or grease trap to prevent excess lubricant ruining the brake linings.

Forces acting on the half-shaft
(1) Shear force due to the weight of the vehicle.
(2) Bending force due to the weight of the vehicle.
(3) Torsional or twisting forces due to the driving and braking torques.
(4) Side thrusts as the vehicle turns a corner.

Three-quarter floating, Fig. 8.13
The bearing is mounted *on the casing* and is held against a shoulder by a lock-nut and tab washer. The hub is made in two parts, the inner part fitting *over* the bearing and also enclosing a spring-loaded oil seal. The outer part may be integral with the half-shaft, be a splined and interference fit upon it, or be secured to the shaft by a taper, key and lock-nut. The brake drum may be integral with the hub outer half or secured to it by countersunk-headed set screws. The back-plate mounting flange is nearer to the centre of the axle than in the semi-floating designs.

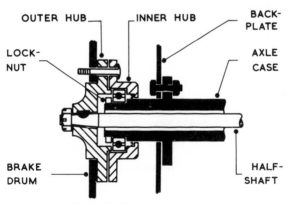

Fig. 8.13   Three-quarter floating

Forces acting on the half-shaft

(1) Bending load due to side thrust when cornering.

(2) Torsional (twisting) forces due to the driving and braking thrusts.

Fully floating, Fig. 8.14

This is a design generally used in commercial vehicles. The hub is a heavy forging or casting of steel and is carried *on the axle case* by two

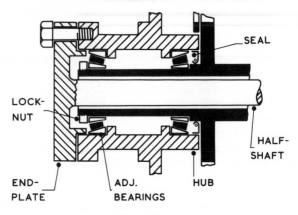

Fig. 8.14   Fully floating

heavy-duty opposed taper-roller bearings. The tracks of these bearings are located by shoulders and a lock-nut, and are adjustable. The hub drive plate is integral with the shaft and is secured to the hub by radially arranged set bolts, a gasket being fitted between the two. A spring-loaded oil seal is fitted into the inner side of the hub near the back-plate flange.

Forces acting on the half-shaft

In these designs the half-shaft is subjected only to torque loads resulting from the driving and braking thrusts. The half-shaft may be removed without removing the wheel.

Note. In *all* of the designs described the fracture of a half-shaft will result in the loss of driving torque due to the action of the differential unit.

The Braking System

Function

The brakes of a vehicle have to absorb all the energy given to the vehicle by the engine plus that due to the momentum of the vehicle. This energy must then be wasted or dissipated. In most vehicle brakes the energy is absorbed by friction, converted into heat, and the heat dissipated by the stream of air passing under and around the vehicle. As the energy is absorbed, the vehicle is slowed down; in other words, its motion is retarded. The brakes must also pull up the vehicle smoothly and in a straight line. The road wheels may be retarded, or braked, by means of drum or disc friction brakes, or by a friction brake which is applied to some part of the transmission system.

Mechanical brake assembly, Fig. 9.1

These are mounted at the ends of the axles and each consists of a non-rotating back-plate and shoe assembly which is enclosed by a drum. The drum rotates with the road wheels, and the back-plates are bolted rigidly to the stub axles and to the ends of the rear axle case.

Two shoes are mounted on each back-plate and each carries a friction lining of an asbestos material. Some linings are riveted to the shoes by copper or brass rivets, while others are secured by means of a chemical bonding process. The shoes may be thin steel pressings or aluminium alloy castings but they must be rigid and they must absorb and dissipate heat quickly. They are fitted between an expander unit, which is free to move slightly on the back-plate, and an adjuster unit which is riveted to the back-plate. The shoe ends are fitted into slots machined in the ends of both the expander and adjuster tappets and the shoes are forced towards each other by two strong springs. The braking torque is transmitted to the axle by the rigid adjuster and back-plate.

Operating systems

The power to operate the brakes may be provided by the manual effort of the driver or by the driver's effort with some assistance from a servo unit. In some heavy vehicles the brakes may be fully power operated by the engine.

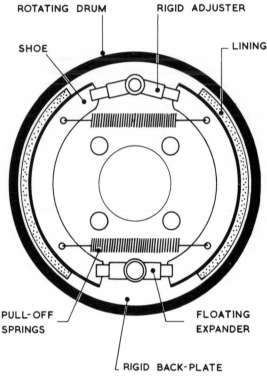

Fig. 9.1   Mechanical brake assembly

Motor-car brakes have to be so designed that they can be operated properly by drivers large and small, and by women as well as men. The maximum force needed at the pedal to fully operate the brakes should not be greater than about 180 N, yet the force needed at the brake shoes may exceed 4450 N. This force multiplication is obtained by a series of levers in which each lever increases the force by reducing the movement (principle of moments).

In servo-assisted and fully powered systems the forces acting at the shoes are made proportional to the effort made by the driver. In this way he is allowed to 'feel' the effects of his braking.

The brakes may be operated by cables or rods, or by an hydraulic system. In all systems the pedal force is multiplied and directed equally to the shoe assemblies.

Brake compensation

The great disadvantage of the *simple* rod- or cable-operated braking system is that it is impossible to guarantee that the forces operating the shoe assemblies will be all the same, and if they are not then the brakes will be inefficient. They will also be very dangerous because the vehicle will be pulled out of its intended path whenever one shoe assembly is operated either before the others or with greater force. The systems which followed were greatly improved in this respect by the inclusion of compensators. The arrangement and form of these units vary but their principle of operation is that of the simple balance beam. Although the complete mechanical system is no longer used in cars as a main brake it is used as a parking brake, and in a more complicated form is used in some other vehicles.

It should be noted that, as the system of levers is used to increase force by reducing movement, mechanical systems are made less efficient by wear at all the pivot points. This may be reduced by maintaining the system in tension, and by maintaining the correct angularity of the levers.

A further disadvantage of the simple braking system is that the front brakes cannot be made to do most of the work of retardation by applying them with greater force than the rear brakes, although they have the greater contact with the road because of the weight transfer which takes place as the brakes are applied.

Principle

Although the compensators used in vehicle brakes are quite compact, their principle of operation is the same as that of the balanced beam. In Fig. 9.2 a brake is arranged to be operated by the movement of each end of the beam. If a force is applied to the centre of the beam, and shoes A contact their drum before shoes B make contact with theirs, the beam will pivot about the end A and so pull on brake B. The applied force is divided equally between the brakes because it is applied at the centre of the beam; i.e. at the same distance from each brake lever.

This action takes place very quickly and so prevents one brake being applied either before or with more force than the other.

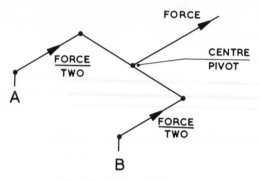

Fig. 9.2   Balance beam

Practical compensators, Fig. 9.3
These consist of a short, vertically arranged, tube which has a double lever welded to its lower end and a single lever welded to its upper end. The levers are arranged at right angles. The rods from each brake assembly are connected to the ends of the double lever by forked ends and clevis pins, while the rod from the central compensator is similarly connected to the single-ended lever. The tube is free to pivot on a vertical shaft carried at the end of a link which is itself pivoted on the axle or spring plate. When the brakes are applied the levers and the link pivot to divide the applied force equally between the two shoe assemblies.

This type of compensator is widely used in the hand or parking brake system. This system must operate independently of the main brakes to meet legal requirements.

Fluid system
The mechanically operated systems have generally been replaced by fluid systems, or some form of power-operated or power-assisted system.

System layout
The system consists of a fluid tank or reservoir, a master cylinder, a

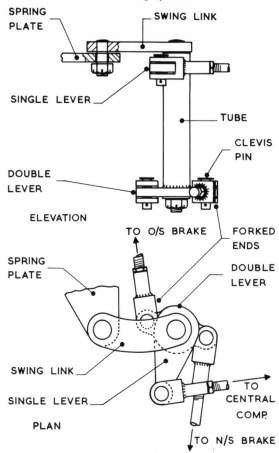

Fig. 9.3 Brake compensator

system of rigid and flexible pipes, pipe junctions, and wheel cylinder assemblies. The reservoir may be combined with the master cylinder. The wheel cylinders may operate shoes and linings or disc pads. A pressure-operated switch, which controls the brake warning lamps, is usually fitted at the first junction from the master cylinder.

Air must not be allowed to remain in the system, so air bleed nipples are fitted at the wheel cylinders and sometimes at the master cylinder.

The force applied to the pedal pad is magnified by the leverage of the pedal and is converted into pressure by the piston of the master cylinder (force divided by area = pressure). This pressure is applied to one part of an enclosed system but is at once transferred to all other parts of the system. The pistons of all the wheel cylinders then convert the pressure

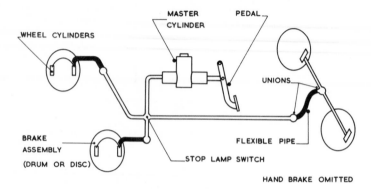

Fig. 9.4   Lockheed fluid brake system (hand brake omitted)

into an increased force which moves the shoes to contact the drums and so retard or stop the vehicle. The braking or retardation force is arranged to be directly proportional to the applied pedal force.

Fluid systems operate effectively because:
(1) For most practical purposes a fluid cannot be compressed; this is illustrated in Fig. 9.5.
(2) A pressure cannot be applied to one part of an *enclosed* system without the same pressure acting equally at all parts of the system. The principle of hydraulic operation is illustrated in Figs. 9.5 and 9.6.

Due to these two features the fluid brake system is automatically fully compensated; i.e. automatically divides the available braking force equally between the shoe assemblies. No separate compensators are required, there is no lost motion due to friction, and there are no linkages to wear or rattle. By law, however, a separate rod- or cable-operated hand brake is required. Fluid systems require little modification to meet the requirements of independent suspension arrangements.

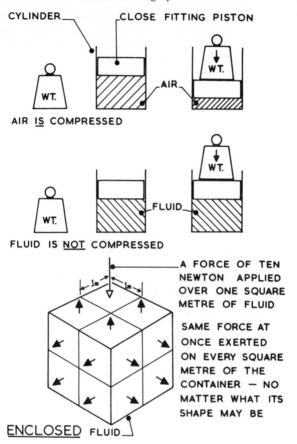

CYLINDER — CLOSE FITTING PISTON

AIR

AIR **IS** COMPRESSED

FLUID

FLUID **IS** **NOT** COMPRESSED

A FORCE OF TEN NEWTON APPLIED OVER ONE SQUARE METRE OF FLUID

SAME FORCE AT ONCE EXERTED ON EVERY SQUARE METRE OF THE CONTAINER — NO MATTER WHAT ITS SHAPE MAY BE

ENCLOSED FLUID

Fig. 9.5   Action of fluid pressure

Should air be present in the system these features are rendered ineffective and the brakes will not operate properly. This is because air can be compressed, and the pedal force will be wasted in doing this and not be transferred fully to the wheel cylinders. This fault is known as 'spongy pedal' and the air must be expelled by 'bleeding the system'.

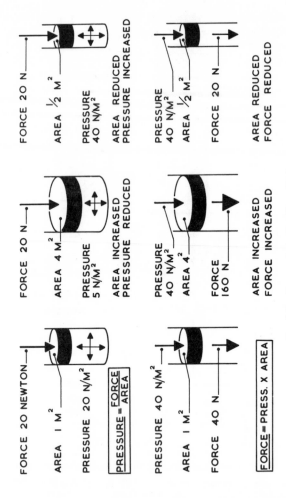

Fig. 9.6　Forces in hydraulic cylinders

The master cylinder (Lockheed), Fig. 9.7
Function
The master cylinder converts pedal force into a pressure which is
applied equally and at the same time to each of the wheel cylinders.

Construction
The unit consists of a cast iron (or aluminium alloy) cylinder with

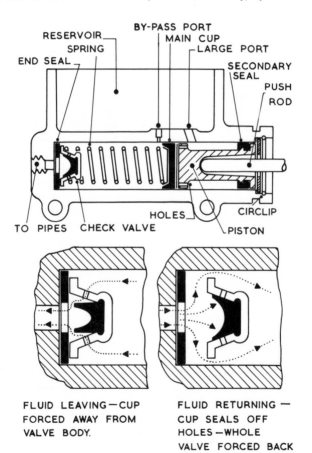

Fig. 9.7   Master cylinder

mounting lugs for attachment to the chassis or scuttle. The bore is accurate in size and fine in finish, and contains a piston with main and secondary rubber cups. A double-acting check valve controls the flow of fluid to and from the pipe system and is normally held to a rubber seal in the end of the cylinder by a long spring. The other end of the spring is located by a cup spreader fitted inside the main rubber cup. The pressure face of the piston has a ring of small drilled holes and the piston operates in fluid at all times. This latter feature reduces cup wear and the possibility of air entering the cylinder. A large hole, or port, supplies fluid to the rear of the piston while a small, or by-pass, port connects the forward portion of the cylinder to the reservoir.

Operation

(*a*) *Brakes applied.* When the pedal is depressed the push rod moves the piston up the cylinder, pushing the main cup before it. The movement of the cup causes its edges to make a pressure-tight seal against the cylinder wall and, when the cup passes the by-pass port, the fluid in the forward portion of the cylinder is totally enclosed. Further pedal motion then increases the pressure on this fluid until it exceeds the pressure maintained in the pipe-line system. This static pressure is about 55 kN/m^2 and is controlled by the spring acting on the check valve. When the cylinder pressure exceeds the line pressure, the small rubber cup inside the check valve is forced away from the body and *at once* the higher pressure acts in the wheel cylinders, forcing their pistons outward and in turn forcing the shoes to press hard against their drums.

Continued pedal motion forces fluid through the check valve into the pipe-lines and maintains or increases the shoe-operating pressure in spite of the outward movement of the wheel cylinder pistons. As the shoes rub against their drums the energy of the vehicle (due to its motion) is converted into heat which is carried away by the cooling air stream. As the energy is absorbed and dissipated so the motion of the vehicle is reduced or stopped.

(*b*) *Brakes released.* When the pedal is released the push rod is withdrawn by the action of the pedal-return spring. The piston spring forces the piston to return very quickly and this creates a sudden pressure drop in the forward part of the cylinder. At the same time the difference between the two pressures forces fluid to flow through the holes in the piston face from the rear part, so reducing the back pressure upon the piston and helping to provide a quicker release of the brakes.

The fluid in the pipe lines is now at a higher pressure than that in the cylinder, and the shoe pull-off springs are forcing the wheel cylinder pistons to move inward. Fluid returns to the master cylinder, but as the small holes in the check valve are sealed by the small rubber cup, the whole valve assembly is forced away from the rubber end seal. The larger fluid-return hole thus made available also assists in the quicker release of the brakes. The returning fluid enters a cylinder which is full of fluid but not under pressure. This fluid is forced through the by-pass port back into the reservoir. (This is the small jet of fluid seen when bleeding the brakes.) The displacement of fluid by the returning fluid ensures that the cylinder is always full and ready for use. It also compensates for any small fluid losses and for the expansion of the fluid.

The returning action continues until the line pressure is equalled by the loading of the piston spring. At this point the spring is able to close the check valve down upon the end seal and so isolate the cylinder from the pipe-lines, a pressure of about 55 kN/m^2 being maintained in the lines. The check valve has two functions:
(1) To maintain a standing pressure in the system which enables the brakes to operate at once.
(2) To ensure that any leak will be of fluid from the system (which is easy to detect) and not of air being drawn into the system. Air entry is difficult to locate and the presence of air makes the brakes unreliable and dangerous.

DRUM BRAKES

In these types the shoes and their operating and adjusting mechanisms are enclosed by a drum which rotates with the wheel, and are mounted upon a circular back-plate bolted rigidly to either a front stub axle or the rear axle case.

Lockheed front brake (2LS)

The shoes are of T-shaped cross-section and are made of steel. Each carries a lining of asbestos material which is riveted or bonded to it. One end of each shoe has a semi-circular notch into which is fitted the cam of the 'Micram' adjuster; the other end of each shoe is radiused.

Between the shoes, and diametrically opposite each other, are shoe-operating cylinders of cast aluminium alloy. These are sealed at one end and are bolted rigidly to the back-plate. Each cylinder contains a piston, a rubber cup, a plastic cup spreader, and a small spring. The outer ends of the pistons are slotted and carry the adjuster forks of the adjuster assembly. The radiused ends of the shoes are fitted into flat-bottomed grooves in the sealed end of the cylinders. The shoes are held to the cylinders, and to the back-plate, by springs.

The upper or rearmost cylinder is usually connected to the fluid system by a flexible hose of large diameter but small bore. A metal pipe is fitted to connect the two cylinders and the second cylinder, being the farther from the master cylinder, is fitted with a bleed nipple.

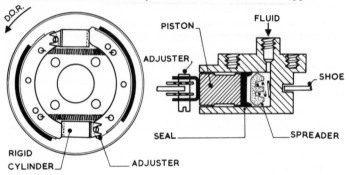

Fig. 9.8   Lockheed front brake   Fig. 9.9   Lockheed cylinder

Leading shoe

Where the expander forces a shoe outwards in the same direction as the rotation of the drum the resulting friction causes the shoe to force itself harder against the drum, i.e. the shoe has a self-applying or self-servo action. Such a shoe is called a leading shoe and, in a leading and trailing shoe assembly, the leading shoe provides about three-quarters of the total retarding force.

Trailing shoe

Where the expander forces a shoe outwards in the opposite direction from the rotation of the drum the resulting friction forces the shoe away from the drum. This is called a trailing shoe. Such shoes provide only about one-quarter of the total retarding force of the leading and trailing shoe assembly.

Two different shoe assemblies may be used. These are:
(1) The leading and trailing shoe assembly (L&T).
(2) The two-leading shoe assembly (2LS).

Lockheed rear brake (L&T), Fig. 9.10
Construction
The two shoes are both held in position by a slotted and rigidly mounted anchor plate which transmits the torque reaction forces from the shoes to the back-plate and the rear axle case. A single operating cylinder is fitted between the ends of the shoes diametrically opposite the anchor plate and slightly below the rear axle. The cylinder is free to slide in a slot cut in the back-plate. Two different springs are used to hold the shoes to the anchor and to the back-plate, the single coil spring being fitted across the anchored ends of the shoes.

The cylinder is an aluminium-alloy casting and has one end sealed. This end is slotted to locate the moving end of the trailing shoe. The cylinder contains a piston, a rubber cup, a plastic cup spreader, and a small spring. The piston is made in two halves, the inner half having a flat face which is sealed by the rubber cup. The outer half carries a metal dust excluder and is slotted to support a 'Micram' adjuster. A pivoted lever, operated by the hand brake, is arranged so that its shorter end fits between the two halves of the piston, the inner faces being slotted for this purpose. As the lever and its pivot are exposed to the rear of the back-plate they are enclosed by a rubber boot. The cylinder is fitted with a bleed nipple.

Adjustments
During service the only adjustment which should be necessary is that of compensating for lining wear. The wheel is lifted clear of the ground and each shoe adjuster turned to lock the drum. It is then slackened back carefully until the wheel can rotate freely. The hand brake cable may require shortening by a screw adjustment to compensate for cable stretch. The pedal must have about 13 mm of free play to make sure that the main cup of the master cylinder is clear of the by-pass port.

Bleeding
This should only be necessary if a part of the system has been disturbed or if the reservoir level has been allowed to fall so low that air has entered the master cylinder.
(1) Adjust all shoes correctly.
(2) Fill the reservoir and keep topping up as the operation is carried out.
(3) If the master cylinder has a bleeding nipple, slacken this and press

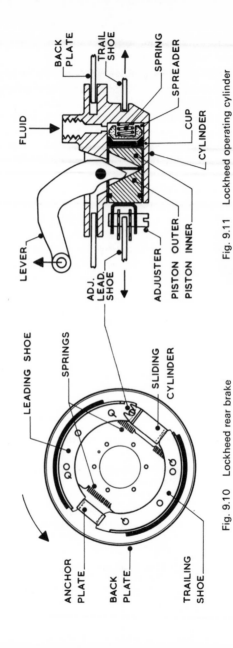

Fig. 9.11 Lockheed operating cylinder

Fig. 9.10 Lockheed rear brake

the pedal slowly by hand. Tighten the nipple while the fluid is flowing and before the end of the stroke.

(4) Fit the bleeder pipe to a wheel cylinder nipple on the back-plate of a rear brake with the pipe end under the surface of a small quantity of fluid in a glass jar.

(5) Slacken the nipple and depress the pedal. Allow the pedal to return freely.

(6) Repeat the operation until no air bubbles can be seen in the jar. Lock the nipple with the pedal in the down position.

(7) Refill the reservoir and repeat the operation with the other rear brake and then the front brakes.

Note. Always put fresh, clean fluid into the reservoir – expelled fluid always contains air bubbles. Allow to stand for 48 hours before using again.

Faults in fluid brakes

Table 9.1

Fault	Cause
No braking	Shortage of fluid in reservoir and master cylinder. Main cup perished. Broken pipe
Spongy pedal	Air in system. Linings not bedded in to drums. Part-worn linings mixed up during repairs. Master cylinder mounting bolts slack. Weak drums – if skimmed
Excess pedal movement	Shoes or pedal need adjustment. Master cylinder bolts slack. Pedal pivot worn. Leaking pipes or unions. Main cup worn
Pulling to one side	Oil on linings at opposite side. Uneven tyre tread or pressure. Distorted drum. Flexible pipe blocked – internal cracks. Loose back-plate, spring mountings, or spring U-bolts. Worn steering joints
Grabbing brakes	Shoes need adjusting. Scored or distorted drums. New linings. Shoes seized on pivots. Loose road spring mountings
Drag – not releasing	Shoe adjustment too tight. No pedal clearance (by-pass port closed all time). Seized expanders or hand brake cables. Swollen rubber cups

DISC BRAKES

Girling disc brake, Fig. 9.12
Construction
The disc is made of cast iron and is bolted to the wheel hub, so that its
flat surfaces are vertical. An inverted, U-shaped caliper of cast iron is
fitted over the disc and is bolted to the stub axle assembly. This assembly
therefore acts as a torque arm which resists the reaction forces from the
braking torque. Each side of the caliper contains a fluid cylinder and a
piston, a rubber piston sealing ring set in a recess in the cylinder wall, a
dust cover, and a pad assembly. The cylinders are interconnected by a
bridge pipe or by a drilled hole, the one nearest the master cylinder being
connected to the system by a flexible hose. The cylinder farthest from the
master cylinder is fitted with a bleed nipple.

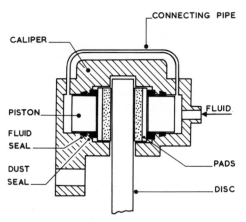

Fig. 9.12   Girling disc brake

Each pad assembly consists of a steel back-plate to which is bonded a
segment-shaped pad of special friction material. The pads are located
and retained in the caliper by bolted-on retainer plates, or lock pins.

Some calipers are made in two parts and are bolted together. They
must never be split during normal service but this may have to be done
(to replace the piston seals) during a complete overhaul. Disc brakes
usually have the same life as an engine, e.g. about 80 000 km.

Operation

When the brakes are applied, and little or no wear has taken place, the slight piston movement necessary is obtained without relative movement between the piston and its seal, i.e. the piston movement distorts the seal. When the brakes are released the seal regains its shape and retracts the piston – maintaining a light rubbing contact between the pads and the disc. This contact is due to the combination of the friction between the seal and the piston, and the static head of brake fluid, i.e. this is a 'hydro-static' brake.

When wear has occurred the piston moves slightly through its seal to take up a new position in the cylinder, i.e. it automatically compensates for the wear, and the hydrostatic effect automatically ensures the correct light rubbing contact when the brakes are released.

Service

System. The fluid system requires the normal service procedure.

Pad wear. Pad wear may be checked by direct inspection, stripping of the assembly not being necessary. Pads should be replaced when worn down to about 3 mm thickness.

Disc wear. After a very long period of service the discs may be found to be badly scored, distorted, or to suffer from surface cracking. Faulty discs should always be replaced by new units.

Note.

(1) The disc brake has no self-servo action, so higher operating forces and pressures are required. In spite of this feature the disc brake, particularly when used with a hydraulic servo unit, provides a braking effort which is directly proportional to the applied pedal force.

(2) The higher operating forces required complicate the design of the hand brake mechanism. For this reason many cars are fitted with disc brakes at the front wheels only.

10 Batteries

Electrical systems

As seen in the vehicle, the complete electrical system appears to be most complicated but only five main systems or circuits are used. They are named according to their functions and may be identified by a system of colour coding of the cables. The circuits are those used for:

(1) Starting.
(2) Ignition.
(3) Lighting.
(4) Auxiliaries.
(5) Battery charging.

Each circuit has its own particular electrical devices and, with the exception of the charging circuit, all draw the electricity needed for their operation from one large battery. The battery does not store electricity itself, however, but contains chemical substances which make electricity by their interaction.

Conductors and insulators

Electricity will only flow through an unbroken circuit and only through materials known as *conductors*. A good conductor is a material which offers very little resistance to the flow of electricity through it, silver, copper and aluminium being good conductors. Weak acids and certain chemical solutions will also conduct electricity. Other materials offer varying degrees of resistance, and some offer so much that electricity will not flow through them at all. The materials in this third group are known as *insulators*, examples being rubber, fibre, mica, porcelain and some plastics. The air gap between the contacts of a switch is also an insulator – so preventing the flow of electricity by breaking the circuit.

Potential difference

The chemical action of each cell produces a difference of electrical pressure between its two terminal posts. This difference is termed *potential difference* (p.d.) and is measured in volts. It may also be known as electrical pressure or *voltage*. Each cell of the lead–acid type produces a voltage or pressure difference of 2 volts when fully charged, and by inter-connecting groups of 3, 6 or 12 cells it is possible to provide pressure differences between the end terminals of 6, 12 or 24 volts respectively. It is this pressure difference which causes a flow, or *current*, of electricity to pass between the terminal posts of the battery through a complete path, or *circuit*.

For most practical purposes the positive battery terminal is considered to be at the higher potential or voltage, and electric current is thought of as flowing through the circuits from the positive to the negative terminals.

A cell consists of two plates or rods, of different materials, which are immersed in a chemical solution. The plates are called *electrodes* and are usually made of zinc, copper, lead or carbon. The solution consists of chemicals dissolved in water (for example, sulphuric acid) and is called the *electrolyte*. There are a number of different chemical cells but they all have the ability to cause an electron stream to flow as a result of the chemical actions which take place between the different materials in the cell.

Primary cells are those in which the chemicals are permanently changed, or exhausted, by their use in producing an electron stream and electric current. When these cells are exhausted, or discharged, they are replaced.

Secondary cells are those in which, after discharge, the chemicals can be restored to their original chemical nature and state. This is done by passing an electric current through the cell in the opposite direction from the current produced by the cell; i.e. the electron stream is reversed and therefore the chemical action is reversed. This reversal is called charging the cell.

The secondary cell

The most common secondary cell is the lead–acid type in which the electrolyte is sulphuric acid dissolved in pure water and the electrodes are lead grids in plate form. When the plates are first formed the grids are filled with a paste of lead oxide and sulphuric acid. They are then fastened together and immersed in large lead-lined baths containing a solution of sulphuric acid. Two groups of plates are immersed in each bath and an electric current is passed through the plates and the acid for about 96 hours. During this time the plates at which the current enters the bath have their lead oxide paste changed into lead peroxide and so become positive plates. This is due to the combination of the lead oxide with the oxygen set free from the sulphuric acid solution by the passage of the current through it. At the same time hydrogen is set free by the current and this combines with the lead oxide of the other group of plates to form water and change the paste into spongy lead. The plates are then removed from the bath, washed and dried, and are ready to be built into cells.

A simple lead–acid cell consists of a positive plate filled with a paste of lead peroxide and a negative plate filled with spongy lead (see Fig. 10.1). Both are immersed in a solution of sulphuric acid in water and because the materials are different, and because the acid is in solution, a charge, or potential difference, exists between the two plates or electrodes. When fully charged the potential difference or e.m.f. is about 2 V.

Action
(*a*) *Discharge*, Fig. 10.1. When the electrodes are connected by an

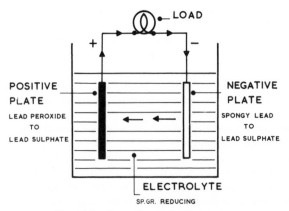

Fig. 10.1   Secondary cell: discharging

external conductor the circuit is completed through the electrolyte. The electron stream and the current associated with it pass through the circuit. The chemical energy of the cell is then released in the form of electrical energy.

The current passes through the cell from negative to positive and in so doing ionises the electrolyte. The positively charged hydrogen ions pass to the positive plate where they give up their electrical charges and combine chemically with the oxygen of the lead peroxide to form water. At the same time the negatively charged sulphion ions combine with the lead of both plates to form lead sulphate. Oxygen is also set free which combines with hydrogen to form more water. As the active materials of the plates gradually become the same, and the electrolyte becomes weaker, the electron stream and the potential difference are reduced and so the voltage of the output current is also reduced. In practice the cell, or the battery of cells, should not be discharged beyond about 1·8 V because:

(1) Lead sulphate occupies a greater volume than lead peroxide and excessive sulphation may cause the plates to buckle or the paste to fall out.

(2) Lead sulphate is a hard gritty substance which acts as an insulator and is therefore difficult to remove if allowed to build up excessively.

(*b*) *Charge,* Fig. 10.2. When the cell is exhausted, or discharged, it is re-charged by passing through it a current in the opposite direction from the discharge current. This ionises (or breaks down) the water of the electrolyte into its constituent ions. The hydrogen ions pass to, and combine with, the sulphion ions of the negative plate, so changing its paste from lead sulphate to spongy lead and forming sulphuric acid. Some of the oxygen ions pass to the positive plate and combine with the lead sulphate to form lead peroxide, while the remainder combine with some of the hydrogen and the displaced sulphion ions to form more sulphuric acid.

Note that on discharge the solution becomes weaker as water is formed and on charge becomes stronger as acid is formed. The strength of the electrolyte is, therefore, a very good indication of the state of charge of the cell. This strength may be checked by the use of the hydrometer. It should also be noted that the hydrogen and oxygen ions will only combine chemically with the other materials of the cell for as long as the lead sulphate is being reduced to lead peroxide and spongy lead. When this reduction is completed hydrogen gas will be given off at the negative plate and oxygen at the positive plate. This gassing is a visual sign that charging is complete. Further passing of current will only decompose the water of the electrolyte and necessitate topping-up the cell with distilled water.

THE VEHICLE BATTERY

This consists of 3, 6, or 12 cells connected in series to provide 6-, 12-, or 24-volt currents. Each cell consists of a number of positive plates which are connected together and have a common terminal post. As the material of the positive plates always has the greater volume variation, every positive plate is sandwiched between two negatives. This ensures the more even working of the positive plates and reduces the tendency to buckling. The two groups of plates are interleaved so that positive and negative alternate. The plates are prevented from contacting each other by separators of ebonite, cedar wood, porous rubber, or a special form of porous plastic. The plates are made as close together as possible to help reduce the internal resistance of the cell (Fig. 10.3).

The group of plates is fitted into a compartmented case of a tough and acid-proof material, usually being suspended by the connector

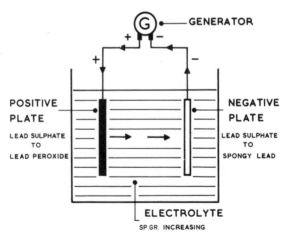

Fig. 10.2   Secondary cell: charging

GRID FILLED WITH LEAD PEROXIDE = POSITIVE PLATE
GRID FILLED WITH SPONGY LEAD = NEGATIVE PLATE
(a)

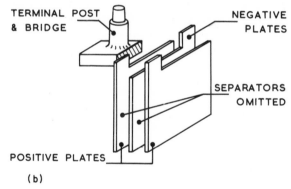

Fig. 10.3 Battery plates: (a) battery grid; (b) plate assembly

bridge so that the bottoms of the plates rest on ridges on the bottom of the case. This is to prevent sediment causing a short circuit between the plates. The top of the plate assembly is enclosed by a moulded cover which is sealed to the main case by pitch or a similar material. Arrangements must be made for filling up with electrolyte and topping-up with distilled water. Screw stoppers are often used but many modern car batteries have patent devices which permit only the correct level of electrolyte to be obtained. Whatever device is used, it is most important that it allows the cell to be vented to the atmosphere to prevent the build up of pressure due to gassing or changes of atmospheric pressure. It must also prevent the escape of acid spray.

The connections between the cells are in the form of lead bars. These may be on the top of the case but modern practice is to have them under the top cover. This increases the cranking ability by reducing the internal resistance, reduces short circuits, and makes it easier to keep the battery clean and dry.

Electrolyte

Composition

The electrolyte is a solution of concentrated sulphuric acid in distilled water. To obtain the correct strength of solution the acid and water must be mixed in the correct proportions and this can only be checked by the use of the hydrometer (see p. 169). A rough proportion with which to start mixing is 1 part of acid to 3 parts of water by volume. Commercial concentrated sulphuric acid has a specific gravity of 1·835 and this must be reduced to the specific gravity recommended by the battery manufacturer – usually between 1·260 and 1·270 at 15·5 °C. (See 'Specific gravity', below.)

Precautions

The mixing must be done in a large acid-proof vessel and it is extremely important to remember to add acid to the water and not water to acid. This is because the mixing produces a considerable amount of heat. If the acid is added to the water, the mass of the water absorbs the heat and all is well. If, however, water is added to the acid, the heat produced will cause the acid and water to be thrown out of the vessel with such violence that the person doing the mixing is certain to receive acid burns.

The mixing must be done slowly, the acid being added in small quantities and being well stirred with a glass or plastic stick. After allowing time for cooling, the specific gravity is checked by the hydrometer. The reading is taken at the bottom of the curve of the surface of the liquid in the tube and the reading corrected for the temperature variation. At 15·5 °C the reading should be 1·260. The correction is to add 0·004 to the reading for every 5·5 degrees above this figure and to subtract 0.004 from the reading for every 5·5 degrees below 15·5 °C.

Acid burns must be washed at once and treated with a solution of bicarbonate of soda or a special cream. If blisters appear they must not be broken and should be examined by a doctor. If this work is done regularly, protective clothing and boots should be worn and protective cream applied to exposed skin. The eyes must always be protected by goggles or a plastic shield.

Specific gravity

The specific gravity of a substance is the ratio between the mass of a certain volume of the substance and the mass of the same volume of water; i.e. it is a comparison between the density of the substance and the density of water. The specific gravity of water is the standard and is taken to be 1. If the specific gravity of a substance is said to be 1·2 this means that it is 1·2 times as dense as water. The specific gravity of liquids can be determined by the use of a suitable hydrometer.

The hydrometer, Fig. 10.4

The hydrometer commonly used for vehicle batteries consists of a graduated glass float fitted inside a glass or plastic tube. The upper end of the tube is sealed by a rubber bulb and the lower end is fitted with a small-bore rubber pipe. In use the lower end of the pipe is immersed in the electrolyte of the cell, the bulb depressed and released, and a small quantity of the electrolyte drawn up into the tube. The float rises and finds its own level. In water it will rise to a certain level which is marked on its scale as 1. In the electrolyte it should read between 1·200 and 1·350, depending upon the state of charge of the cell. The usual scale is graduated from 1.150 to 1.400 and may also be marked by coloured bands indicating discharged, half-charge, and fully charged.

Several precautions must be taken when using an hydrometer. These are:
(1) Keep naked flame away from the battery – do not smoke.
(2) Check that the float is free to move in the tube and that the instrument and battery top are clean. Hold the instrument vertical.
(3) Check that the battery has not just been topped-up.
(4) Correct the reading for temperature variation (see 'Temperature effects'). The scale is graduated at a standard temperature of

15·5 °C and will read higher than correct at temperatures below this, and lower at temperatures above this standard.

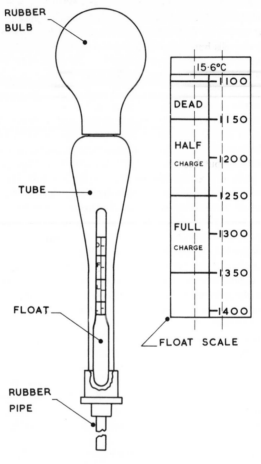

10.4   Hydrometer

Temperature effects

At normal temperatures (15 °C–26 °C) the specific gravity of the electrolyte of most vehicle batteries is about 1·265 when they are first filled. When fully charged the specific gravity should be between 1·270 and 1·290, slight variations existing between different makes. A battery with a specific gravity of between 1·190 and 1.210 may be considered to be about half charged, while a reading of about 1·100 to 1·120 means that the battery is fully discharged. There may be slight variations between the cells but a large difference in the reading taken from one cell indicates a fault in that cell.

When under a load of light and ignition systems, the voltage per cell should be about 2·00 for a fully charged battery. When the battery is discharged the voltage will fall to about 1·75 V.

The battery is an electrochemical device, and as temperature has an effect on chemical actions it also has an effect upon the operation of the battery. Within limits, the higher the temperature the greater the battery output because the chemical actions are speeded up. A further point is that the porous plate separators will pass the acid more easily at higher temperatures and this reduces the internal resistance of the cells. Where batteries are operated in hot climates it may be advisable to reduce the specific gravity of the electrolyte to prolong the life of the plates. The reduction is usually 30 points; i.e. a fully charged battery should read 1·240 to 1·260.

As the temperature falls the chemical actions are slowed down, the specific gravity of the electrolyte is increased, and the lead of the negative plates becomes less spongy. These factors result in the battery output falling as the temperature is reduced. For this reason the battery manufacturers specify a battery which will be capable of providing an adequate starter motor cranking speed at temperatures of about $-6\,°C$ when the battery is about three-quarters charged.

Under normal winter conditions the electrolyte in a fully charged battery is not likely to freeze, and even that in a half-charged battery would not freeze until temperatures below $-25\,°C$ were reached. In a discharged battery, however, the electrolyte would freeze at about $-8\,°C$, a temperature not uncommon in winter in this country. In cold weather, therefore, batteries should be kept well charged to avoid physical damage to the battery itself as well as inconvenience to the vehicle user.

The best operating temperature for a battery is about $30\,°C$.

Sulphation

This is the formation of lead sulphate on the surfaces of both the positive and negative plates and is the result of the *normal* discharge action of the cells. Lead sulphate is a hard, white, gritty substance which does not conduct electricity. If it is allowed to build up it will result in the complete and permanent failure of the battery. Sulphation increases the internal resistance of the cells and so reduces the capacity and output voltage of the battery. *Excessive* sulphation may be caused by the following:

(1) Prolonged discharging.
(2) Local chemical action in the cells due to the entry of dirt and impurities.
(3) Insufficient or infrequent charging.
(4) The electrolyte level being too low.
(5) The specific gravity of the electrolyte being too low.

Storage
In the normal way sulphation is reduced almost at once by the charging current from the vehicle dynamo and so has no chance to form a hard and insulating skin over the active material of the plates. When a battery is to be stored for some time, however, special precautions must be taken to prevent it being damaged by sulphation. The battery must be topped-up with distilled water and be fully charged by a bench charger. It must then be carefully cleaned and dried and the terminal posts covered by white Vaseline to prevent corrosion. Batteries should always be stored in a cool, dry place free from sunlight as they will discharge themselves over a period of time, the rate of discharge increasing as the temperature increases and in the presence of dirt and moisture. In all cases a freshening charge should be given once per month during storage to reduce the chances of sulphation damage to the plates.

Battery capacity
The capacity of a battery depends upon its mechanical and chemical condition, its age, the areas and numbers of plates, and the specific gravity and temperature of its electrolyte. The capacity is limited to the *useful* output of the battery over a number of hours and it is measured in ampere/hours. When making a comparison between batteries on a capacity basis it is most important that the same basis be used for each. It is usual to specify the number of hours and the discharge voltage at which the time is measured, the hourly rating being either 10 or 20 and the final voltage being 1·8 V per cell.

Definition

The capacity of a battery is the number of ampere/hours which can be obtained in a continuous discharge which lasts for 10 hours, starting with the battery fully charged and stopping when the voltage has fallen to 1·8 V per cell.

Example. A battery which has a capacity of 80 ampere/hours at the 10-hour rating must be able to supply 8 A for at least 10 hours before its cell voltage falls below 1·8 V.

The same battery on the 20-hour rating would have a capacity of about 96 ampere/hours and would have to be able to supply 4·8 A for at least 20 hours before its cell voltage fell to 1·8 V.

Voltage variation, Fig. 10.5

During charge

When a fully discharged battery is re-charged at the normal rate, i.e. at a number of amps which is one-tenth of the ampere/hour capacity at the 20-hour rate, the cell voltage rises from about 1·8 V to 2·1 V in the first hour of charging. It then remains between 2·1 V and 2·2 V for the next 3 hours and then rises to about 2·6 V over the last 6 hours. After standing for a few hours the voltage will fall to the normal value of about 2·1 V per cell.

During discharge

When a fully charged battery is discharged at the normal rate the cell voltage falls fairly quickly to about 2·1 V and remains at that value for the next 7 hours. It then falls over the last few hours to less than 1·8 V – when discharging should be stopped to avoid the excessive sulphation of the plates.

If heavier currents are taken from the battery, the period of time of discharge before the voltage falls to 1·8 is of course less, and vice versa. The starter motor may require currents of between 200 A and 300 A to rotate the engine crankshaft. It is important that its use is not prolonged or the battery will be over-discharged and may be permanently weakened by the overheating and buckling of the plates.

Battery charging

A battery which is in good condition but in which the specific gravity of the electrolyte has fallen to about 1·180 must be recharged on the

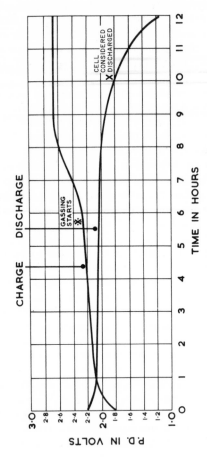

FOR A 100 AMP/HOUR BATTERY. CHARGED AT 11 AMPS
FOR 10 HOURS. DISCHARGED AT 10 AMPS FOR 10 HOURS

10.5   Voltage variation

bench at the normal rate for its type. The charging system of the vehicle is only designed to maintain the charge level of the battery and cannot fully charge a battery which is fully discharged.

The battery vent stoppers are removed and the electrolyte levels corrected by adding distilled water until the tops of the plates are covered. The charging current (which must be d.c.) must be passed through the battery in the opposite direction from its own current so the bench positive lead must be connected to the battery positive terminal. The current is switched on and adjusted to the correct rate by means of a variable resistance. Charging is continued until all the cells are gassing freely and the specific gravity of each has reached a maximum value. This point is reached when three consecutive hydrometer readings, at hourly intervals, have shown no change. The levels should then be re-checked and adjusted. If distilled water has been added, then the charge should be continued for a short time to obtain a thorough mixing of the water with the acid. Acid itself should never be added at this stage and should never be required unless the battery has been upset and the acid spilt. The current is then switched off and the battery carefully cleaned and dried ready for installation in the vehicle.

Portable fast chargers are available for garage use but these should not be used for routine charging instead of the slower bench charging system. Fast charging is an emergency treatment only, but provided that the manufacturer's instructions are carried out the battery will not be harmed. One of the more important features of battery charging is that the temperature of the cells and electrolyte must not exceed about 38 °C. These chargers have a temperature-sensitive switch which must be placed in a central battery cell and which will cut off the charging current when this temperature is reached. Failure to use this device can result in the active material of the plates falling out. This occurs at about 60 °C and is caused by the expansion of the grids under the heat produced by the passage of relatively large currents through the cell. A good battery can be brought up to full charge in about 1 hour but such charging of any one battery should be very infrequent.

Battery testing
Two main tests are usually carried out on vehicle batteries.

Hydrometer test
The state of charge is determined by the use of the hydrometer. As

already explained (p. 169), this instrument measures the specific gravity of the electrolyte which varies with the state of charge of the cell. The electrolyte of each cell in turn is tested and corrections made for the temperature difference between that of the electrolyte and the standard of 15·5 °C. A cell giving a reading between 1270 and 1290 is considered to be fully charged, between 1190 and 1210 half charged, and between 1100 and 1120 fully discharged.

High-rate discharge tester
The condition of the battery when operating under a load is determined by the use of the high-rate discharge tester. This instrument consists of two prongs which are connected by a bar or rod of low resistance. A good-quality centre zero voltmeter is connected across the resistance bar, the scale being marked to show cell condition as well as volts. The test loading for car batteries is about 150 A and for commercial vehicles and tractors is about 300 A. Each cell in turn is tested by connecting the prongs across the plate linkages of the cell and allowing current to pass for about 10 seconds. A sound cell will give a steady reading of between 1·2 V and 1·5 V. If the reading falls rapidly a weak cell is indicated. Note that as this is a severe test the time limit must not be exceeded. The high-rate discharge tester must not be used on a battery which has less than 70% of its full charge.

Precautions
(1) Do not take hydrometer readings immediately after adding distilled water to a cell. Charge to gassing point to thoroughly mix the water with the acid.
(2) The high-rate discharge test will not give a reliable indication if the battery has just been taken off charge. When checking the battery of a vehicle which has just been driven, operate the starter motor once or twice to remove the surface charge. This is the cause of the possible error.

Cadmium test
A third test could be carried out but this is not normally done in vehicle workshops. This is the cadmium test and its purpose is to determine the chemical condition of the plates, that is, to determine the potential difference of the positive plates above zero and the negative plates below zero. The instrument consists of a cadmium stick and a cell-testing voltmeter. The stick is enclosed by a perforated ebonite tube

(which is immersed in the electrolyte) and is connected to the negative side of the voltmeter. The other side of the voltmeter is connected first to the positive and then to the negative plate linkages. The two voltmeter readings are then added to obtain the potential difference between the plates, noting carefully whether or not the negative plate reading is plus or minus.

Precautions

The battery must be on charge or discharge because open circuit or no load readings are not a reliable indication of the true condition of the plates.

When a sound battery is nearing the end of a charge the 'cadmium stick to positive plate group' reading should be about $+2.5$ V while the negative plate group reading should be about -0.14 V – the total voltage difference, or potential, being 2·64 V. An unsatisfactory chemical condition of the plates is indicated if the cadmium-to-positive reading is much below 2 V and the cadmium-to-negative reading is positive instead of negative by more than about 0·3 V.

Test results and meanings

Table 10.1

Specific gravity	High-rate discharge	Meaning
All cells within the limits of 1270 to 1290	All readings high and held for 10 seconds	Cells are all sound and well charged
All cells within limits of 1190 to 1210	All readings low but held	Cells all sound but only half charged – bench charge needed
One cell 0·030 or more below others	Falling reading in cell having low hydrometer reading	Weak cell may be failing or be partly sulphated – may revive under a long low charge
Readings all different and more than one cell 0·050 below normal	Readings all different and more than one reading falling rapidly	Battery needs replacing
All readings below about 1100	All readings around zero	Plates badly sulphated – may respond to a long low bench charge but doubtful

Battery installation

The following points should be taken into account when battery mounting arrangements are being considered:

(1) The battery should be easy to reach and inspect because regular attention is required.

(2) The battery must not be subjected to excessive vibration or shaking because of the construction of the plates. The mounting clamps must not be overtightened nor yet be so slack as to allow the battery to move in its box or frame.

(3) The battery must be reasonably near to the starter motor to permit the use of short lengths of cable. This is to reduce the unavoidable volt drop which reduces the power available to operate the starter. This consideration applies to all vehicle wiring circuits.

(4) The battery must not be fitted too near to the exhaust manifold and pipe. This is because higher temperatures increase the rate of chemical activity in the cells and so may reduce the life of the battery. The electrolyte levels will also need to be checked more often.

Battery service

The battery should have the following attention at regular intervals:

(1) Check the electrolyte level of each cell and fill up to the tops of the separators with distilled water.

(2) Keep the battery top and terminals clean and dry, together with surrounding metal. Remove corrosion or spilt acid by means of boiling water or dilute ammonia or soda solutions. Wash them with clean water and dry thoroughly. Cover bare metal with Vaseline or an acid-resistant paint.

(3) Check that the vent plugs are clean and that the vent holes are free from obstructions. Replace missing plugs at once.

(4) Remove the skin of black, gritty lead from the terminals and the inside of the connectors. Smear with Vaseline and replace. Do not overtighten clamp bolts or self-tapping screws. Do not hammer terminals or connectors.

(5) Check that the connection to the chassis or frame is both clean and tight.

Precautions

(1) Do not smoke or bring a naked flame near to batteries, especially during or just after charging.

Table 10.2 **Battery faults**

Symptom	Fault	Causes	Cures
1. Headlamp brilliance less than normal 2. Brilliance varies with engine speed 3. Starter motor sluggish in operation 4. Difficult engine starting	Battery in a low state of charge	1. Insufficient vehicle use 2. Excessive use of current 3. Low electrolyte levels 4. Slack fan belt 5. Loose connections in charging circuit as a whole 6. Regulator requires adjustment 7. Dynamo in need of service or repair	Bench charge battery at normal rate Check and rectify charging circuit, dynamo, and regulator Check control box complete
1. Frequent topping-up required 2. High specific gravity readings 3. Lamp bulbs burning out or blackening 4. Positive sides of cell top cover plates lifting	Battery is being over-charged	1. Regulator and cut-out in need of adjustment 2. Excessive use of a trickle charger	Readjust to the manufacturer's settings Restrict use of charger or reduce the rate of charge
1. Excessive sediment in electrolyte 2. Visible signs of buckled plates 3. Plates white in colour after a prolonged charge	Plates are excessively sulphated – possibly permanently	1. Insufficient charging 2. Electrolyte levels neglected 3. Battery left in uncharged condition	A long and low charge may remove the excessive sulphation, depending upon how hard and thick it has become

(2) Disconnect the earthed cable before working under the bonnet if the work will permit this.

(3) Never place tools on the battery top.

(4) Switch off charger before disconnecting the battery.

Battery additives

These additives, or dopes, are often advertised as improving the performance or prolonging the life of the battery. In almost all cases their use either damages the plates or has no worthwhile effect upon them. The guarantees of most battery manufacturers are cancelled if their batteries are found to contain any of these additives.

Battery faults, see Table 10.2.

Electrical symbols

In vehicle wiring diagrams it is necessary to have a clear and easily drawn means of identifying different parts of a circuit. The standard method of drawing the various common parts of a circuit is shown in Fig. 10.6, and this method is a recognised British Standard. It is worth studying these diagrams before starting the next chapter.

In a simple lamp circuit (Fig. 10.7) the positive battery terminal is connected by a cable to one contact of a switch or circuit breaker. The other switch contact is connected to one side of the lamp filament by a second cable. The other side of the filament is connected to the battery negative terminal by a third cable which completes the circuit.

While the switch contacts are open the circuit is broken by their air gap. The chemical action of the battery does not take place, no electrical energy is produced and no current flows to cause the lamp to light.

When the switch contacts are closed, the circuit between the battery terminals is completed. The chemical action takes place in the battery cells, electrical energy is produced and the voltage or pressure difference forces current to flow through the circuit from the positive to the negative terminals – so lighting the lamp.

Series and parallel circuits

Where several electrical units are to be included in a circuit it is possible to arrange them either in series or in parallel (see Fig. 10.8).

In the series arrangement, 10.8(a), the current flows through each unit in succession. It follows, therefore, that the same number of amps passes through each unit. The voltage across each unit will depend

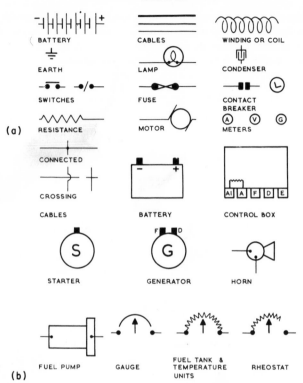

(a)

(b)

Fig. 10.6   Electrical symbols: (a) general; (b) vehicle

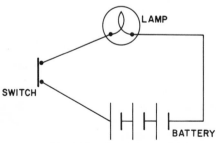

Fig. 10.7   Simple lamp circuit

upon the resistance offered by the unit; the higher the resistance the higher the voltage. Any extra unit fitted into a circuit will increase the total resistance of the circuit and so reduce the current flowing through the whole circuit, thus reducing the efficiency of operation of the units.

In the parallel arrangement, Fig. 10.8(b), the voltage across each unit is always the same. The total current flow is divided between the units. The number of amps passing through each unit is in inverse proportion to its resistance; i.e. if one unit has twice the resistance of another it will carry half the current of the other. Any unit later included in the circuit, in parallel, will have the effect of reducing the total resistance of the circuit and increasing the total flow of current.

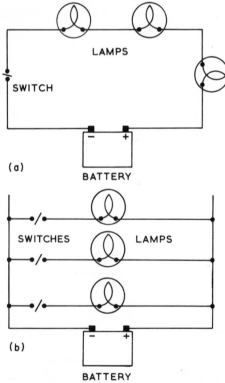

Fig. 10.8   Types of circuits: (a) series; (b) parallel

Cables and Lamps

The cables used in vehicle circuits are classified according to the diameter and numbers of wires used to form the cable. For example, a cable having 14 wires, each of which is 0·30 mm in diameter, is classed as a 14/0·30 mm cable.

A further classification is made according to the insulating and protective coverings used. These are:
(a) vulcanised india rubber, or V.I.R.
(b) tough rubber sheath, or T.R.S.
(c) armoured cable, or A.C.
(d) cab tyre sheath, or C.T.S.

These coverings are used for all types of cable. The usual insulation for most cables consists of a rubber covering applied directly over the cable. This is covered by a cotton braided sheath which is itself covered by a skin of cellulose. Some of the more modern cables have plain copper-stranded cores covered directly by plastic (PVC).

The number of strands, or wires, in a given diameter of cable determine the current-carrying capacity of the cable and therefore the purposes for which it is suitable.

Voltage drop
When an electric current is passed through a conductor the resistance of the conductor causes a drop in the voltage; i.e. the potential difference causing the current to flow is reduced. It is, therefore, more important that consideration be given to the current and voltage requirements of electrical units when these are being connected by new or replacement cables.

Example. A unit requires 12 V and 3 A for its efficient operation. If the battery voltage is 13·5 V and the total resistance of the circuit cables is 1 ohm, will there be sufficient voltage to operate the unit properly?

Total resistance = 1 ohm
Amps to operate = 3 A
Battery voltage = 13·5 V

Using Ohm's Law the volt drop will be $R \times I$. This is 1×3 V, so the voltage available to operate the unit is $13·5 - 3 = 10·5$ V. As the unit is designed to operate at 12 V, it cannot operate properly.

Current-carrying capacities

The number and diameter of wires (in mm) forming the core of a cable will each safely carry maximum currents as shown in Table 11.1.

Table 11.1

Cable (mm)	Maximum load (amps)
9/0·30	4
14/0·30	7
28/0·30	14
44/0·30	22
37/0·90	60
61/0·90	83
61/1·10	175

The cables required in most 12-volt systems are as shown in Table 11.2.

Table 11.2

Purpose	Cable (mm)
Feed circuits from the battery to the switches	44/0·30
Charging, headlamps, horn circuits	28/0·30
Accessories, side and tail lamps, feed ignition circuits	14/0·30
Starter motor cables	61/0·90 37/0·90 61/1·10
High-voltage ignition cables of 7 mm outside diameter of 9 mm outside diameter	12/0·40 40/0·30

Some of these ignition cables are also suppressed to avoid interference with the radio and with television sets. Note that the total volt drop in any circuit should never exceed 10% of the battery voltage. Where long lengths of cable are unavoidable, always use a cable of greater than nominal current-carrying capacity to reduce the volt drop.

Circuits

Three different systems of wiring are possible in vehicle circuits. These are:

(1) The double-pole or insulated-return system.

(2) The single-pole or earth-return system.

(3) The three-wire or balanced-load system.

In the first system, see Fig. 11.1(a), insulated cables or conductors are used to carry the current away from each unit as well as to supply it to the unit.

In the second system, Fig. 11.1(b), the chassis is used to provide the return circuit to the battery. This system saves money, is less complicated, and is lighter in weight than the insulated return. It is just as efficient provided that a good electrical contact is made between each unit and the chassis or body to which the battery is connected.

In the third system, Fig. 11.1(c), a neutral cable is taken from the battery centre – so providing 6 V or 12 V on either side. This system, by careful arrangement of the loads, balances the loads on each side and no current should flow through the neutral cable. This system is usually employed on Public Service vehicles where the lighting loads are much greater than those of other vehicles.

Colour codes

Most manufacturers adopt a system of colour coding to assist in the quick recognition of cables. These usually consist of single-colour cables for main feeds to switches, the same colour being used as a tracer from the switch to the unit. Earth-return cables are black. A simplified version of the Lucas system is:

Brown: for battery feeds to the control box and ammeter. Also to the lighting and ignition switches, and auxiliaries.

Yellow: for dynamo circuits and warning lamp.

Green: for ignition-controlled and fused auxiliaries.

Blue: for headlamp circuits (see Fig. 11.2).

Red: for side and tail lamp circuits. Also for other lamps used only when side lamps are switched on. (See Fig. 11.3.)

Black: for all connections to the chassis for earth-return purposes.

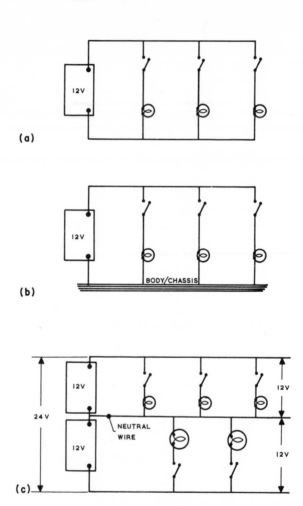

Fig. 11.1   Circuits: (a) double-pole or insulated-return; (b) single-pole
or earth-return; (c) three-wire or balanced-load

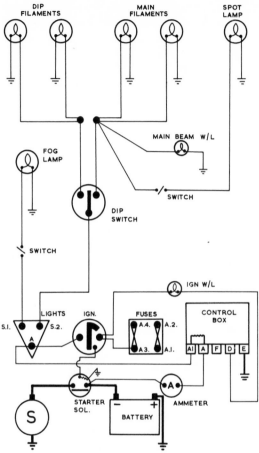

Fig. 11.2   Headlamp circuit

Short circuits

These occur when the insulation of a cable is damaged. Some or all of the current escapes into the chassis to return to the battery without operating a unit correctly. The large current which can flow may cause a fire by overheating the cable.

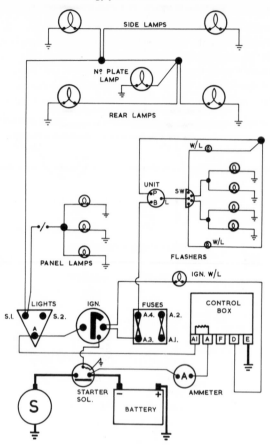

Fig. 11.3   Other lamp circuits

Cable connectors, Fig. 11.4

For a number of years the connections between units and cables were made by means of spade or eyelet terminals. These were soldered to the cables and attached to the units by screws or nuts and lock washers. The disadvantages of this method are:

(1) The screws or nuts are liable to be slackened by vibration.

(2) The core of the cable is liable to break at the junction with the terminal.

(3) Corrosion from the soldering flux attacks the cable under the insulation near the terminal.

(4) It is a slow and expensive method.

A later method was the use of snap connectors. These consist of small, ball-ended tubes which fit over the insulation and are soldered

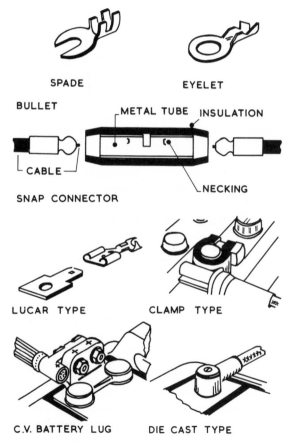

Fig. 11.4   Cable connectors

to the end of the cable core, the end projecting slightly through the ball-end of the tube. These tubes, or bullets, are fitted into insulated tubes which are of a slightly larger internal diameter and necked to snap into place behind the ball-end of each bullet. Snap connectors are available to make joints between two, four, or more cable ends. These connections have good mechanical and electrical properties, and are easy to make and break. The connection to units is made by fitting the bullets into rolled phosphor-bronze strips riveted to the units.

An improved version of the snap connector abolished the need for soldering, the bullet being crimped to the cable by specially designed pliers.

In the modern Lucas systems the connectors are called 'Lucar' terminals and in these the cable end is attached to a flat phosphor-bronze sleeve by means of resistance welding. This is a much stronger and quicker process than soldering. The edges of the sleeve are rolled over and a central portion is slotted to act as a spring. The male half of the terminal is a flat phosphor-bronze blade and may be a part of an electrical unit. The sleeve is fitted over the blade and a snap action is obtained as a small pip on the sleeve engages with a small hole in the blade. A 35-A version is used for charging circuit connections, while 12-A versions are used for all other connections.

Because they carry the largest currents, connectors for starter cables are the strongest and heaviest on the vehicle. The terminal posts of car batteries are formed into short, tapered cylinders, the positive post being larger in diameter than the negative. The older type of connector was a lead- or cadmium-coated brass clip which was clamped to the terminal post by a nut and bolt, the starter cable or earth strap being secured either by two screws or by soldering. The modern type is a die-cast block of lead which is formed around the end of the cable, fitting over the terminal post and being secured by a self-tapping screw.

The cable connectors of the heavier vehicles consist of heavy leaden lugs which are formed on the cable ends. These lugs are bolted- to terminal posts of mating shape.

Fuses

The fuse is a device placed in a circuit to protect the cables and units from damage by the passage of excessively high currents. These currents may result from a short circuit in either the cables or the units, the fuse being a deliberately weak point. Car and light commercial vehicle fuses are nearly all of the cartridge type, Fig. 11.5(a), in which a short length of low-melting-point wire is enclosed by a glass tube. The ends of the tube are closed by metal caps to which the ends of the wire are soldered. the fuse is secured by clips to an insulated base, the cable-ends being connected to the clips.

The wire is an alloy of lead and tin, or lead and copper, which will pass only a certain maximum current. If a current in excess of this should pass, the wire will overheat and melt, so breaking and protecting the circuit. Inside each fuse is a small label indicating the current it will pass, each circuit being protected by a different strength of fuse. When a fuse has 'blown' it is most important that the fault causing it to fail is found and rectified before fitting a replacement fuse. The spare fuse clips should be refilled at the same time.

Commercial vehicle fuses may be of the wire or strip type. The wire type, Fig. 11.5(b), consists of a small insulated plate to which are riveted two metal prongs. The fuse wire is stretched between these prongs and the plate clipped into the fuse block. In the strip type, Fig. 11.5(c), the fuse wire is replaced by a thin pressing secured to the block by knurled terminals.

Fuse ratings

In the earlier Lucas systems the fuses were mounted on the control box. Two fuses (each of 35 A rating) were fitted, one controlling all of the accessories which operated independently of the ignition switch and labelled 'Auxiliaries', and the other controlling those circuits in which the ignition switch acted as a master switch. The latter fuse was labelled 'Aux–Ign'. The starter and road lamps are not normally fused.

In the later systems these fuses are rated at 50 A for the auxiliaries and 35 A for those ignition controlled. Car radios should be fused separately.

The Lucas fuse rating and identity is given in Table 11.3.

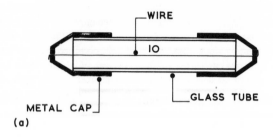

(a)

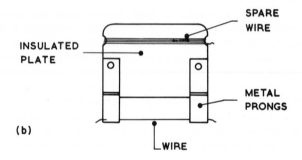

(b)

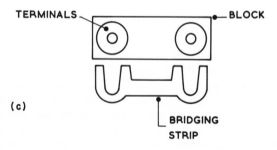

(c)

Fig. 11.5   Fuses: (a) cartridge type; (b) wire type; (c) strip type

Table 11.3

Rating in amps	Label colour
5	Red print on yellow paper
10	Green print on black paper
15	Black print on light brown paper
25	Black print on pink paper
35	Black print on white paper
50	Purple print on yellow paper
60	Yellow print on red paper

Light

Medium

Light is radiated energy and a substance through which light can pass is called a medium; e.g. air, water and glass. If the medium is homogeneous (i.e. has the same properties at each and every point) then light will pass through it in a straight line. Light may also be absorbed or reflected by a body. Polished surfaces are good reflectors and dull surfaces are good absorbers of light. An important fact to remember is that we see most bodies by the impression their *reflected* light makes upon the nerves of our eyes. When the medium contains large numbers of tiny particles, as in dusty conditions and fog, each particle reflects light in a different direction with the result that the reflected light is broken up, or diffused, to such an extent that we cannot see objects clearly.

Sources

The main source of light is the sun, moonlight being reflected sunlight. Up to the development of electrical power, all artificial light was obtained by the combusion of materials which contained hydrogen and carbon, the light given out being due to the glowing or incandescent, particles of carbon in the flame. These materials include wood, vegetable and animal fats and waxes, coal gas, acetylene, and petroleum products such as paraffin and naphthalene. Acetylene gas burns with a brilliant white flame, and as it is relatively easy to produce and store it was used in the lamps of the early motor-cars.

Electric light

The first source of artificial light which did not involve combustion became available when electricity was found capable of heating a fine wire to such an extent that it glowed. The simple lamp bulb consists of a small coil of fine tungsten wire (the filament) enclosed by a glass bulb filled with an inert or non-combustible gas such as argon. The tail of the bulb is cemented into a brass cap which supports the bulb in the bulb holder. One end of the filament is connected to the cap while the other end is connected to a lead contact which is in the end of the cap but insulated from it.

As the current passes through it, the filament first radiates the long infra-red waves, and although these cannot be seen they can be detected as heat. As the filament itself becomes hotter the radiated waves are reduced in length and the filament glows a dull red. The waves then become shorter and shorter and the glow changes through bright red to yellow and finally to a brilliant white-hot light. The reverse sequence occurs when the current is switched off. As the gas filling of the bulb will not support combustion, the filament does not itself burn and the bulb has a relatively long service life. Vibration, shock and electrical overloads are the main sources of bulb damage.

Quantity

The quantity of light given off by a source is measured in terms of *candle power*. One candle power is the light produced by the burning of a standard candle, this being a candle made from sperm whale oil which weighs $\frac{1}{6}$ lb and burns at the rate of 120 grains per hour. The modern standard is now based upon the light emitted by a hot body at a known temperature. The unit is the *candela* and melting platinum has an intensity of 60 candelas per square centimetre.

Inverse square law

The intensity of light upon a surface is *directly* proportional to the power of the source, and is *inversely* proportional to the square of the distance between the source and the surface; i.e. if the distance from the source is trebled the light intensity will be one-ninth of the original intensity.

Road illumination

The ability of a driver to *see* distant objects or surfaces illuminated by his headlamps does not follow the inverse square law because the light rays have to travel to the objects and then be *reflected* back into his eyes. The amount of light so reflected depends upon the colour, size and roughness of the surfaces, and the effects of this reflected light will also vary with the condition of the nerves in the driver's eyes. In practice, therefore, the power of the headlamp bulbs must be many times greater than the theoretical value for illumination at the normal reach of the beams.

It is important that the headlamps should provide an *even* intensity of light, or illumination, of the road ahead of the vehicle. The longer-reaching portions of the beam must therefore be of a much greater power than the portions which illuminate the road immediately in front of the vehicle. These important features are obtained by the use of optical devices which, by bending the light rays, produce a beam of light of the correct shape and intensity.

AUTOMOBILE LAMPS

In spite of the great variation in the purpose, shape, size and location of the many lamps fitted to the modern vehicle, every lamp has some form of body, or case, a bulb and bulb holder, a glass (or lens) and a lens retainer (or rim). The more powerful lamps have scientifically designed reflectors and lenses. All external lamps must be sealed to keep out dirt and water. Where the earth-return system is employed each lamp body must make a good electrical connection to the body or chassis. Each lamp is a part of some electrical circuit and its operation must be controlled by one or more switches.

Bulbs
In practice the different bulbs used are classified according to their electrical ratings and not by the candela power of the light they radiate; e.g. a side-lamp bulb may be rated as a 12 volts 6 watts. The current consumption of a bulb is easy to calculate since 1 watt is the rate at which energy is converted, or 'consumed', when 1 volt causes a current of 1 ampere to flow. In this example the current required to make the filament produce white light is 6 W divided by 12 V, or $\frac{1}{2}$ A. Where two filaments are employed, the rating of the larger is given first.

The shape and size of the cap provides a further classification.
British pre-focus (B.F.P.). In these a circular plate is secured to the cap at right angles to its axis, locating the bulb so that the filament is at the exact focal point of the reflector. Where two filaments are used

a notch is cut from the edge of the plate which matches up with a projection inside the bulb holder. This ensures that the bulb can only be fitted in such a way that each filament is correctly located in relation to the reflector. Pre-focus bulbs are used in headlamps and in some fog and spot lamps. The number of contacts in the ends of the cap corresponds to the number of filaments. The normal headlamp bulb rating is 12 V, 60/45 W.

Small bayonet cap (S.B.C.). These caps have two small pins set at right angles to the axis and 180° apart. Two contacts are employed. A double-filament version, used where two different lights are required from one lamp, has offset pins to ensure the correct location of the filaments in relation to the feed cable contacts; e.g. a 12 V, 21/6 W S.B.C. non-reversible bulb as used for stop/tail lamps.

Single centre contact (S.C.C.). These caps are similar to the S.B.C. types but have one central contact only.

Miniature centre contact (M.C.S.). These are similar to the S.C.C. types but are of a smaller diameter.

Miniature Edison screw (M.E.S.). The caps are formed into a thread in the same manner as flashlamp bulbs.

Lilliput Edison screw (L.E.S.). These are similar to the M.E.S. types but are smaller in diameter.

Reflectors

Light travels through air in a straight line and is reflected, to varying degrees, by every surface it strikes (see Fig. 11.6). If the surface is flat and polished, a ray of light will be reflected from it at the same angle as that at which it strikes it; i.e. the angle of reflection is the same as the angle of incidence. The relationship between the strength of the incident and reflective rays is called the *reflective factor*. Curved and highly polished surfaces act in the same manner, being in effect a series of very small flat mirrors. With such a reflector the rays radiated from a source in all directions are reflected and may be concentrated into a strong beam parallel to the axis of the reflector. A vehicle headlamp reflector has a reflective factor of about 95%; i.e. it only absorbs about 5% of the light which strikes it. These reflectors are paraboloid in shape and are made from glass or metal with aluminised surfaces. The bulb filament is arranged to be on the axis and the beam produced is composed of both direct and reflected light rays.

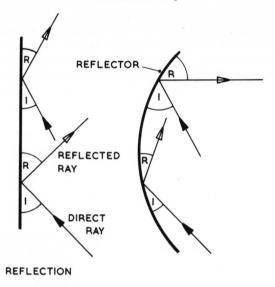

REFLECTION

Fig. 11.6   Reflection of light

Focusing, Figs. 11.6 and 11.7

If the bulb filament is moved along the reflector axis from a point close to the reflector to a point clear of the edge of the reflector, the reflected light will change from diverging rays into a concentrated beam parallel to the axis, and then into crossing and separating rays. At one point only as the filament is moved will the reflected light be concentrated into the parallel beam. This point is called the *focal point* of the reflector and the light rays are said to be focused.

If the filament is positioned below the focal point, the rays will be

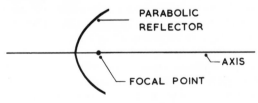

Fig. 11.7   Focusing

concentrated into a weaker beam which passes above the axis. If the filament is positioned above the focal point the beam will pass below the axis; this feature is used for dipping purposes, a double-filament bulb being fitted. These bulbs are pre-focus types and in some vehicles the beam may also be directed to the near side of the vehicle.

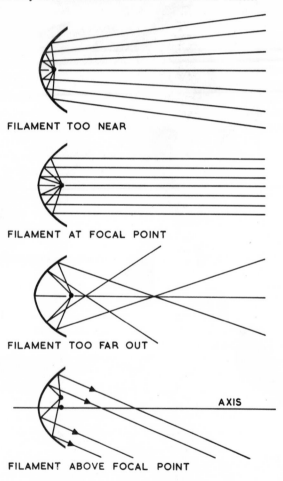

FILAMENT TOO NEAR

FILAMENT AT FOCAL POINT

FILAMENT TOO FAR OUT

FILAMENT ABOVE FOCAL POINT

AXIS

Fig. 11.8   Filament positions

Refraction, Fig. 11.9

Although light travels in a straight line through a homogeneous medium, it is bent, or refracted, when it passes from one medium to another. Refraction is due to the fact that light travels at different speeds in different media. In air its speed is about 299 000 km per second, in water its speed is reduced to about 225 900 km per second, and in glass to about 201 170 km per second. Refraction also occurs when light passes through zones of air at different temperatures and this is the explanation of the pools of water which appear to be on the road on very hot days.

If parallel rays of light are directed upon the side of a glass triangle, or *prism*, they will emerge from the other side still parallel but at a different angle, see Fig. 11.9(a). By altering the angle of the prism they will emerge at a different angle again and in this way the light rays can

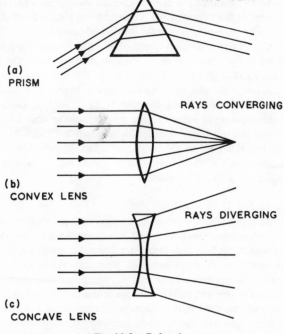

Fig. 11.9   Refraction

be bent to any required angle. Lenses used for headlamps are combinations of a large number of prisms and fluted areas which bend the light rays reflected from the reflector to provide the form of beam desired for both long-range and dipped beams. A *convex lens*, Fig. 11.9(b), will concentrate light rays at a point (focus) while a *concave lens*, Fig. 11.9(c), will make light rays spread out (diverge).

Headlamps

The filament and the reflector together produce a powerful beam of light which is parallel to the axis of the reflector but this beam alone cannot illuminate the road properly. The light reflected by the road must appear to the driver to be of the same intensity at all points and this effect is obtained by the use of some form of lens. The modern headlamp glass is a large number of separately angled prisms and flutes which bend the light rays respectively up or down, or direct them to either side, so providing the correct illumination for each part of the road in front of the vehicle; i.e. a powerful beam for the more distant areas and a more dispersed light for the dipped-beam areas.

The older type of headlamp consisted of a brass or steel case which was bolted to the wing in such a way that the direction of the beam could be altered by pivoting the whole lamp. The light produced by a single-filament bulb was concentrated into a beam by a parabolic reflector of silverplated brass, the rays being focused by sliding the bulb holder inside the reflector. The reflector of the near-side lamp was pivoted inside a frame attached to the lamp body and the whole reflector was tilted by an electromagnet when dipping was needed. At the same time the off-side lamp was switched off. The glasses were usually flat or only slightly moulded.

Light units, Fig. 11.10

The single dipped-beam system was never very satisfactory as half the road illumination was lost, and it was replaced by the double dipping·system in which both lamps are directed down and to the near side. A new type of lamp has been produced which incorporates double-filament pre-focus bulbs and scientifically designed reflectors and lenses. The lens and reflector are made as a one-piece unit and the bulb can only be fitted in one position. The connections to the bulb are made by spring-loaded contacts carried in a cap which locks on to the reflector. The light unit, or reflector and lens assembly, is mounted

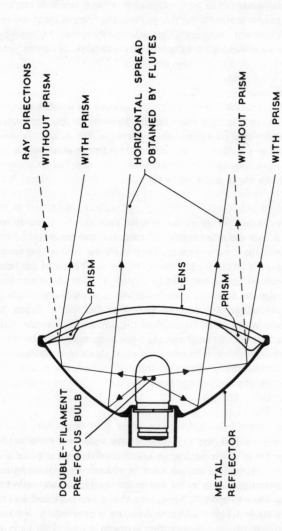

RAY DIRECTIONS

WITHOUT PRISM

WITH PRISM

HORIZONTAL SPREAD
OBTAINED BY FLUTES

WITHOUT PRISM

WITH PRISM

PRISM

PRISM

LENS

DOUBLE-FILAMENT
PRE-FOCUS BULB

METAL
REFLECTOR

Fig. 11.10 Light unit

inside a frame which can be tilted in relation to the lamp body by three spring-loaded screws. The body is fitted flush with the wing surface and the light unit sealed by the rim and a rubber ring-shaped washer. The only adjustment necessary is that of correctly aiming the beam by the adjusting screws which are exposed by the removal of the rim.

Sealed-beam light units

In effect the sealed-beam unit is a special bulb in which a paraboloid, aluminised, glass reflector is sealed permanently to a block pattern lens (Fig. 11.11). The light filaments are correctly located and sealed into the unit which is then filled with an inert gas. The reflector is more efficient than any metal type, and because dirt and water cannot enter the unit it has a long life in service. Should a filament fail, or the lens be cracked, the whole unit must be replaced.

Four-lamp system

The light units in this system are smaller than those previously described and four are fitted instead of two. The two inner units have single $37\frac{1}{2}$-watt filaments and are used to provide the main or long-range beams. The outer units have two filaments, one of 50 W which provides a correctly aimed dipped beam, and a second of $37\frac{1}{2}$ W which provides extra light for the main beam and is below the first filament. Long-range road illumination is therefore provided by all four units and the dipped beam by the large filaments of the outer units; i.e. the main beams have a power of 150 W and the dipped beams of 100 W.

Although this system is more complicated and expensive than the two-lamp systems, the quality of illumination is far superior under all conditions, the great advantage being that each lamp can be designed for one purpose only.

Anti-dazzle

A lamp which is designed to illuminate the road at a considerable distance in front of the vehicle is bound to dazzle an approaching driver. This very serious danger must be reduced or avoided by the use of some system whereby the beams are directed downwards and to the near side. In modern headlamps this is accomplished by two features of lamp design. The beam direction is changed by directing the current through the upper, or dip, filament instead of through the main filament at the focal point of the reflector. The reflected light of

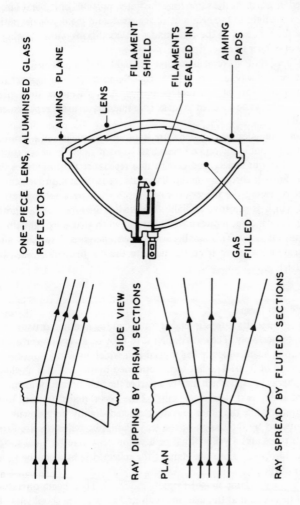

ONE-PIECE LENS, ALUMINISED GLASS REFLECTOR

AIMING PLANE
LENS
FILAMENT SHIELD
FILAMENTS SEALED IN
AIMING PADS
GAS FILLED

SIDE VIEW

RAY DIPPING BY PRISM SECTIONS

PLAN

RAY SPREAD BY FLUTED SECTIONS

Fig. 11.11 Sealed-beam unit

the dip filament is then bent (refracted) by the prisms of the lens, the upper beams being directed downward and the lower beams being directed upward. At the same time the fluted portions of the lens direct more of the light to the near side of the road, and the driver has satisfactory illumination of the road under all conditions without being a source of danger to other drivers.

It is important to remember that the light unit is designed for use in a particular way, e.g. for left- or right-hand drive, and to meet the legal requirements of different countries. A replacement unit must therefore always be checked to make sure that it is an exact replacement optically.

In some vehicles these systems are improved by the use of a dimmer unit. These enable the dipped beams to be used safely in heavy traffic and in poorly lit streets, and consist of a resistance which reduces the current flowing through the dip filaments. A further improvement is that of replacing the driver-operated dip switch by a self-operating switch which is sensitive to light. This switch incorporates a photo-electric cell which generates a small current when struck by light above a certain intensity. This small current then energises a switch which in turn directs current from the main to the dip filaments. (See also Fig. 11.1.)

Fog and spot lamps

These are auxiliary lamps intended for use in fog and fast-driving conditions respectively. They are designed to provide a very powerful and penetrating beam which is flat topped and which has only a moderate side spread of light. The flat top is obtained by the use of a shield of hemispherical shape which may be a part of the bulb or may be arranged in front and over it. This shield cuts off the rays radiated upward from the filament while the other rays are deflected slightly both downward and outward by the design of the lens. Parabolic reflectors are fitted in both types and a yellow bulb or a yellow lens may be fitted to fog lamps to help to reduce the glare of the reflected light from the water vapour particles.

Both types of lamp must be rigidly mounted. Their beam directions should be checked at frequent intervals and their lenses should also be cleaned frequently. It is a legal requirement that these lamps be fitted with their centres not less than 0·6 m from the ground.

Lighting regulations

These legal requirements are rather complicated and the sections which follow are intended as a broad guide only. A more detailed study of an up-to-date regulation should be made when a particular problem arises. (See also Fig. 11.2.)

Headlamps and driving lamps

These must be mounted between 1·2 m and 0·6 m from the ground. They must be incapable of causing dazzle at a height of not less than 1·2 m from the ground at a level distance of not less than 7·6 m from the lamps. As designed and constructed all vehicles meet these requirements, but in service such factors as the loads carried, the settling of the suspension and accidents result in the loss of correct beam alignment. It is, therefore, very important that headlamp alignment checks be made at regular intervals. Fog lamps which are mounted at a height of less than 0·6 m may only be used in fog or when snow is falling. The headlamps should be switched off when the fog lamp is in use.

Side lamps

A white light must be shown forward at each corner at the front of the vehicle. The bulbs must not exceed 7 W and a frosted or diffusing lens must be fitted. These lamps must be at the same height and must be between 0·38 m and 1·2 m from the ground.

Rear lamps

A red light must be shown to the rear at each side of the vehicle and the bulbs must be not less than 6 W. These lamps must be no more than 0·4 m inside the outer edge of the vehicle, must be at the same height, and must be between 0·38 m and 1·2 m from the ground. Reflectors must also be fitted at the rear within the same limits as the rear lights. They must be red and have a minimum diameter of 38 mm.

Rear number plate

This must be illuminated in such a way that it can be read at a reasonable distance, e.g. 18 m.

Reversing lamps

These are not compulsory. One or two may be fitted, but arrangements must be made so that they cannot be switched on except by (a) the movement of the gear lever when selecting reverse, or (b) the use of a separate switch which also operates a warning light. The total power of the bulbs must not exceed 24 W, and the headlamp anti-dazzle regulation applies.

Stop lamps
These are not compulsory but all must operate at the same time and show a steady, diffused, red light to the rear.

Direction indicator lamps
These must be visible at a reasonable distance from both the front and rear of the vehicle, those at the rear showing an amber or a red light. Those which show to the front only must be amber or white, while those which show to the front and rear must be amber only. The flashing rate must be between 60 and 120 flashes per minute and there must be no longer than 1 second's delay after switching on. A warning device must be fitted which operates at the same time as the flashers. The lamps must be fitted between 0·38 m and 2·3 m from the ground and not more than 0·4 m in from the widest part of the vehicle. Their illuminated area must be not less than 0·023 m² and 0·093 m² for vehicles of under 2 tonnes and over 2 tonnes of unloaded weight respectively. The bulb wattage must be between 15 W and 36 W.

Beam alignment
This may be carried out by one of two methods. The first is by the use of a screen or wall marked out to show the correct light beam positions. This is a slow and inconvenient method which has generally been replaced by the use of some form of optical testing equipment.

Screen method, Fig. 11.12
In this the vehicle is positioned on level ground at right angles to, and 7·6 m from, a wall or screen. This is marked out with the theoretical positions of the main beams *when the vehicle is loaded normally*, i.e. with two areas of concentrated light as high as the lamp centres and the same distance apart and arranged equally about a centre line which coincides with that of the vehicle.

The lamp rims are removed to expose the adjusting screws and the beam from each lamp is checked in turn, the other lamp being covered. The top screw provides the vertical adjustment and the two side screws

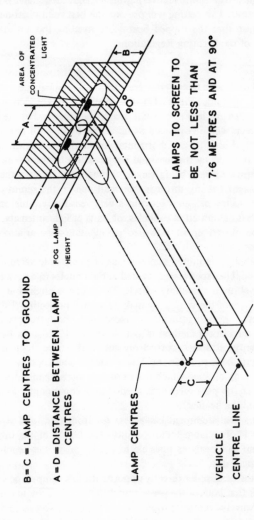

Fig. 11.12 Beam alignment

LAMPS TO SCREEN TO BE NOT LESS THAN 7·6 METRES AND AT 90°

AREA OF CONCENTRATED LIGHT

90°

FOG LAMP HEIGHT

B = C = LAMP CENTRES TO GROUND

A = D = DISTANCE BETWEEN LAMP CENTRES

LAMP CENTRES

VEHICLE CENTRE LINE

the horizontal adjustment. These screws are adjusted until the concentrated light of the beam is covering the marked area and the rims are then replaced. This setting will provide the best road illumination and also ensure that the dipped beams are meeting the anti-dazzle requirements of the Lighting Regulations.

Optical method

Equipment. The Lucas Beamsetter consists of an optical tube and a portable aligning frame (Fig. 11.13). The tube is of square section and has a light-condensing lens at one end. Inside the other end of the tube is a small screen which is pierced at its centre by a small hole. The screen is marked also by one horizontal line and two vertical lines. The beam is reduced by the lens and projected on to the screen, the area of concentrated light being viewed through a window in the top of the tube. Light passing through the small hole in the screen energises a photo-electric cell connected to a very sensitive voltmeter, the scale of which is calibrated in candelas, or units of light intensity. The screen can be moved up or down to compensate for variations in vehicle loading.

The optical tube is mounted so that it may be raised or lowered inside a long, inverted, U-shaped frame secured at right angles to a horizontal frame mounted upon swivelling wheels. The frame is aligned at right angles to the axis of the vehicle by making its two projecting distance pieces contact a wheel-alignment bar placed across both front tyres.

Operation of the optical method is as follows.

(1) Inflate the tyres to their correct pressure and set the steering into the straight-ahead position; i.e. line up the front and rear wheels.

(2) Select an area of floor which does not vary more than 1·5 mm in height over the particular area needed to accommodate both the vehicle and the beamsetter.

(3) Place the wheel-alignment bar across the front tyres and slacken the optical tube clamp handle. Adjust the height of the tube to correspond as closely as possible to the height of the headlamp. Tighten the clamp.

(4) Position the beamsetter directly opposite the first lamp to be tested and check that both of the projecting distance pieces are in contact with the wheel-alignment bar.

(5) Move the screen adjustment lever to obtain the correct setting angle for the loading of the vehicle. This angle is read from the

scale in front of the candela meter (see later note on 'Fine adjustment').

(6) Remove both lamp rims to expose their adjusting screws. Switch the lamps on with the main, or driving, beams selected.

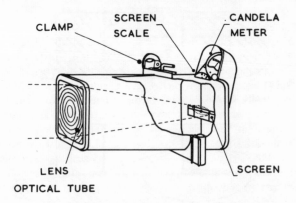

CLAMP   SCREEN SCALE   CANDELA METER

LENS

OPTICAL TUBE

SCREEN

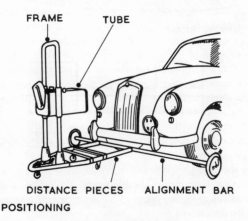

FRAME   TUBE

DISTANCE PIECES   ALIGNMENT BAR

POSITIONING

Fig. 11.13 Optical beam setting

Coarse adjustment
The position of the lamp is adjusted by means of the screws provided until the area of *concentrated* light falls upon the screen equally between

the vertical lines and at each side of the horizontal line, Fig. 11.14(a). The top screw will alter the beam up and down while the side screws will alter it from side to side.

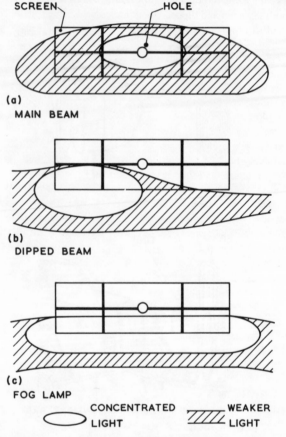

Fig. 11.14   Beam patterns

Fine adjustment

The reading of the candela meter should be noted and the screws further adjusted very carefully until the meter shows its maximum reading.

Dip beam check

The dip switch is operated and the beam pattern on the screen examined. This should show that very little light falls above the horizontal line, Fig. 11.14(b), indicating that dazzle is being avoided.

If both the main and dipped beams are correct, repeat the operation for the other headlamp. Switch off and replace the lamp rims.

Fog lamp

Other lamps are set in a similar manner to headlamps except that the whole lamp may have to be moved. The fog lamp beam pattern on the screen should be below the horizontal line and centred upon the hole, Fig. 11.14(c).

Load and setting angle

The vehicle should be carrying its normal load at the time the headlamps are adjusted and the screen adjustment lever set at zero.

When vehicles are loaded the effect is to lift the beam and perhaps cause dazzle, so this must be compensated when the loads are not present at the time the lamps are adjusted. If car lamps are being adjusted and no passengers are normally carried at night, the screen setting should be zero. If two or more passengers are carried, the setting should be $\frac{1}{2}$ a degree. Commercial vehicle loads vary greatly and experience in the setting of their lamps is the best guide, but the usual settings are between $\frac{3}{4}$ and $2\frac{1}{2}$ degrees.

12 Vehicle Circuits

Earth return

To reduce complication, expense and weight, vehicle circuits do not usually employ return cables from each unit back to the battery. Instead one terminal of the battery and the case of each unit is connected directly to the metal of the chassis and body. These are therefore all at the same electrical potential or voltage as the battery terminal to which they are connected. This is called the 'earth-return system' and it is the battery positive terminal which is connected to the chassis or 'earthed'. The connection is made by means of a heavy cable, or woven copper earth strap, and a bolt. Similar earth straps are used between the engine and the chassis to make certain of getting good electrical contacts.

Main units

The main electrical units of the vehicle are the battery, the starter motor, the starter solenoid switch, the ammeter, the control box or regulator unit, the fuse box, the master light switch, the ignition coil, the ignition distributor and the generator or dynamo. For study purposes these may be represented and arranged as shown in Fig. 12.1.

Current flow

When the generator is not producing electricity at a higher voltage than that of the battery, the battery current flows from the battery positive terminal into the chassis and body to the case of each unit. It then passes through those units in each circuit in which the switch contacts are closed and *returns through the cables* to the control box terminal A. All of the currents employed in the different circuits return through this terminal A, passing through the ammeter, starter solenoid terminal and the battery negative terminal. With the current flowing in this direction the ammeter will indicate the strength of the negative or discharge current, i.e. it will indicate that the battery is being discharged. A warning lamp is always fitted into the circuit and is operated under these conditions.

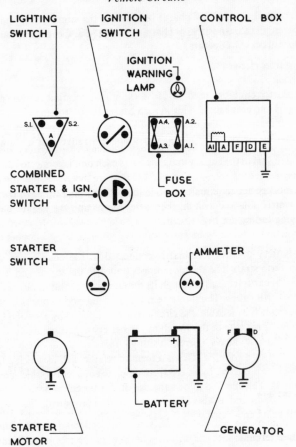

Fig. 12.1   Basic vehicle circuit units

When the generator is producing current at voltages higher than those of the battery, the control box terminal A, and the battery negative terminal connected to it, will be at the higher voltage. The higher pressure will therefore oppose and reverse the direction of the returning current, forcing it to pass through the various switches and units to earth and return to the battery through its positive terminal.

This current reversal will charge the battery, the ammeter will indicate the strength of the positive or charging current and the ignition warning lamp will cease to operate.

The starter circuit
Function

The starter circuit is used to cause the initial rotation of the engine flywheel and crankshaft. This in turn causes the petrol and air mixture to be induced into the cylinders and to be compressed ready for its ignition by the sparking plugs. The simplest arrangement is shown in Fig. 12.2(a).

Units

The modern starter circuits include the battery, the combined ignition and starter solenoid switch, the starter motor and the heavy-current-carrying cables, see Fig. 12.2(b).

Circuit

The battery positive terminal is connected to the chassis and body by an earth strap. The starter motor is bolted to the engine and is connected to earth (chassis) through its mounting flange and bolts and the engine earth straps. The motor terminal is connected to one side of the starter switch by a cable, the circuit being completed by a second cable from the other side of the switch to the battery negative cable.

The flow of heavy current through the circuit just described is controlled by a *solenoid*. This is a form of relay switch in which a thick copper disc is moved, by an electromagnet, to connect two thick copper terminals. This method allows the use of shorter cables which reduces the volt drop and is also cheaper and more convenient, the ignition switch being combined with the starter switch.

Common circuits

All the various currents used on the vehicle flow through the battery negative terminal, the ammeter and terminal A of the control box. A large number of currents also flow through the cables connecting the fuse box terminal A.3, the ignition switch, the light switch terminal and the control box terminal A.1. These cables may be considered as forming a circuit common to all the main circuits.

The solenoid winding is earthed at one end while the other end is secured to a terminal. This is in turn connected by a cable to its own terminal on the ignition switch.

Operation

When the starter switch is operated current flows from the battery positive terminal through earth to the solenoid winding, Fig. 12.2(b). After passing through the winding it returns to the battery negative terminal via the ignition switch, light switch terminal, A.1 and A of the control box, the ammeter and the solenoid battery side terminal.

This small current operates the solenoid, and as the copper disc contacts the terminals the heavy current flows through the starter brushes from earth, passing through the internal circuits of the starter, and returns to the battery negative terminal via the solenoid switch contacts.

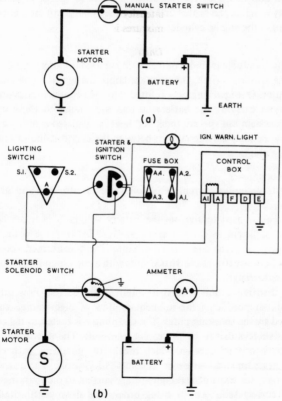

Fig. 12.2   (a) Simple starter circuit; (b) modern starter circuit

The current flow through the internal circuits of the starter motor causes the motor shaft and its drive gear to rotate. In rotating the drive gear winds along the shaft and, still rotating, engages with the engine flywheel so causing the flywheel and crankshaft to rotate. The drive gear is automatically thrown clear of the flywheel and wound back along the shaft when the engine fires.

The ignition circuit

Function

The complete coil ignition circuit is used to provide, at the correct moment and in the correct sequence, a series of sparks of sufficient intensity to ignite the heated and compressed charges of air and petrol mixtures in the engine cylinders.

Units

The ignition system includes the following units: the battery, the control box, the ignition switch, the warning lamp, the ignition coil and the distributor. One sparking plug is fitted into each combustion chamber. The cables carrying the battery current are similar to those of the lighting system but special, thick and heavily insulated cables are used to carry the high-voltage current between the coil, distributor and the sparking plugs.

Functions of units

The battery supplies current to the coil, via the control box and ignition switch.

The coil is used to step up the battery voltage to a much higher voltage, sufficient to cause a spark to jump between the points of a sparking plug in the compressed mixture. The transformed voltage is usually between 10 000 and 16 000 volts with a corresponding reduction in current strength.

The distributor unit is used to interrupt the current flow through the coil, so producing the momentary flow of high-voltage current required by the sparking plugs. The distributor is bolted to the engine and its shaft is driven by the engine camshaft. The distributor shaft operates a contact breaker which breaks the circuit as each engine piston nears top dead centre on its compression stroke. The distributor also directs the transformed high-voltage current to the sparking plugs in the correct sequence, or firing order. The drive shaft rotates an insulated arm between segments set in an insulated cap, each segment being connected to a sparking plug by a specially insulated cable. A similar cable is used to carry the high-voltage current between the rotor arm and the coil.

The sparking plugs are used to introduce into the compressed mixture of petrol and air a spark, or small area of heat, sufficiently intense as to start the mixture burning.

Circuit

The coil should be mounted as close as possible to the distributor to minimise the volt drop. The units are connected in circuit as shown in Fig. 12.3. An ignition warning lamp is connected between the switch or A.3 on the fuse box and terminal D of the control box.

Operation

When the ignition is switched on current flows from the battery positive terminal to earth. If the distributor contact breaker points are open no current can flow through the coil and no high-voltage current will be produced. The warning lamp will be operated by a current passing through it from earth through the earthed generator, the control box D terminal and its cable. This current returns to the battery negative terminal across the ignition switch contacts and through the common circuit.

When the starter motor is switched on and the engine crankshaft is rotated, the distributor contact breaker points will close. Current from earth will flow through them and through the coil to A.3 of the fuse box, returning to the battery through the common circuit. As this current flows through the coil primary winding it establishes a strong magnetic field which also influences the secondary winding.

When the distributor drive shaft cam opens the contact breaker points, the flow of battery current is interrupted. The magnetic field collapses and cuts across the secondary winding, inducing a high-voltage but momentary current in the secondary winding. This current passes to earth through the primary winding, the fuse terminal A.3, the ignition switch and the common circuit to the battery positive terminal.

The distributor is so timed to the engine that at this moment the rotor arm is sweeping across one cap segment connected to a sparking plug. The high-voltage current jumps the gap between the earthed (body) electrode and the insulated centre electrode of this plug and so ignites the mixture in that combustion chamber. As the rotor arm continues to sweep around inside the cap, the battery current through

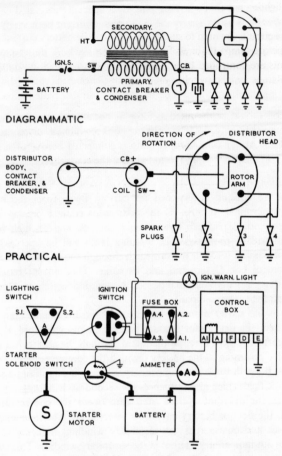

Fig. 12.3   Ignition circuits

the coil primary winding is interrupted to operate each of the sparking plugs in their correct sequence. The high-voltage current returns to the coil secondary winding through the insulated plug electrodes, plug cables, distributor cap and rotor, and cable to the coil high-voltage connection or chimney.

If a negative earth system is used this current flow is reversed.

The lighting circuits

Function

These circuits are used to supply and control the battery current needed to operate lamps required for driving after dark. A number of small circuits are controlled by a master light switch in such a way that the headlamps may be switched on or off, or their beams changed, without affecting the operation of the side, tail and number plate lamps.

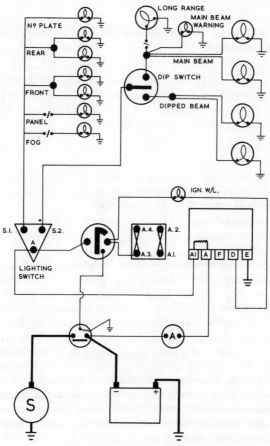

Fig. 12.4   Lighting circuits

Circuits

These circuits are arranged as shown in Fig. 12.4. Terminal A of the light switch is permanently connected into the common circuit, and the switch mechanism is such that the terminals S.1, or S.1 and S.2 may be connected to the terminal A. The terminal S.1 is connected to each of the filaments of the side, tail and number plate lamps, each lamp body and one side of the filament being earthed. The switch terminal S.2 is connected to the dip switch centre terminal while the other two dip switch terminals are connected to the dipped beam and main beam headlamp filaments. The opposite side of these filaments and the lamp bodies are also earthed.

Operation

When a particular lamp circuit is switched on current flows from earth through the case, filament, cables and switches of the various lamps, and returns through the light switch centre terminal to the common circuit and the battery negative terminal.

Auxiliary circuits

Function

These circuits are used to supply and control the current required for the operation of the many electrical units which add to the safety, convenience and comfort of the vehicle user.

Auxiliary circuits and units may be grouped according to the paths taken by their currents to and from the common circuit (see Fig. 12.5). These groups are:

(1) Ignition switch controlled and fused. The units in this group include horns, stop lamps, reverse lamps, direction indicators, screen wipers, heaters, and fuel and water gauges. After passing from earth through the units and switches the current returns to the common circuit across the fuse between the fuse box terminals A.4 and A.3. The fuse is used to protect the units and circuits from excessively high currents which may pass as a result of a short circuit, i.e. parts of the circuit being by-passed due to faulty insulation or other damage. A green cable colour is used to help in the identification of these circuits.

(2) Ignition switch controlled but not fused. This group includes fuel pumps and reserve tank valves, electric chokes, oil pressure warning lamps, overdrives and the control units of automatic transmissions. After passing from earth through the units the current returns to the common circuit through the ignition switch or fuse box terminal A.3.

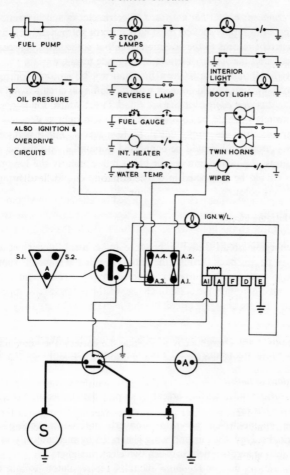

Fig. 12.5   Auxiliary circuits

The identifying colour for this group of auxiliaries is white.

(3) Permanent circuit and fused. Interior lamps, courtesy lamps and boot lamps are in this group. The current returning from these units passes into the common circuit through the fuse box terminal A.1 to the control box terminal A.

(4) Permanent circuit but not fused. Electric clocks and inspection or parking lamp supply sockets must have current permanently available. This current returns to the common circuit at some point between the ammeter and the starter-solenoid battery side terminal.

A radio should have its own fuse and not be ignition controlled. Its return current should connect with the common circuit at A.1.

(5) Light switch controlled and not fused. Panel lamps, fog lamps and their switches should be so fitted that the main light switch acts as a master switch. These units could be regarded as being part of the lighting circuit and should be connected in parallel with the side and tail lamps, the identifying colour being red. Similarly the long-range lamps should be connected into the headlamp circuit, blue being the identifying colour.

The charging circuit

Function

The charging circuit is used to produce and control the current which must be passed back through the battery, while the engine is running, to *compensate* for the current consumed by other four main circuits, i.e. it must maintain the state of charge of the battery. It is important to note that the charging circuit cannot recharge a battery fully.

Units

The units in the charging circuit include the battery, the ammeter, the control box, the generator, and the ignition switch and warning lamp.

Functions of units

The *ammeter* indicates the current, in amps, which is passing either to or from the battery.

The engine-driven *generator* converts mechanical energy into electrical energy, the current being generated by mechanically rotated coils cutting across a field between two electromagnets.

The *control box* or *regulator* includes the regulator itself and the cut-out or reverse current relay. The function of the regulator is to adjust the strength of the charging current to suit the state of charge of the battery. It also prevents the overcharging of the battery and protects the generator against overloading. The cut-out automatically disconnects the generator from the battery whenever the voltage of the generated current falls to a value below that of the battery. In this way it prevents the battery discharging through the generator. When the generator speed is high enough to produce current at a voltage higher than that of the battery, the cut-out contacts close and the generated current is passed through the battery to maintain its state of charge.

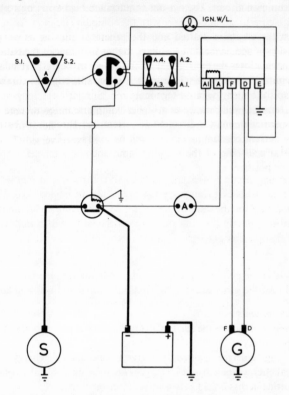

Fig. 12.6   Charging circuit

Circuit

The units are connected as shown in Fig. 12.6. The generator terminals D and F are connected to the control box terminals D and F and the box terminal E is earthed. The ignition warning lamp is connected between the ignition switch terminal A.3 and the terminal D of the control box.

Operation

When the ignition is switched on the warning lamp is lit by the battery current flowing through the generator to the control box terminal D. After lighting the lamp the current returns through the ignition switch to the common circuit. The cut-out contacts are held apart by a small spring.

When the engine is started and the generator runs at its normal speeds it produces current at a voltage higher than that of the battery. This current closes the cut-out points and passes through the regulator to the control box A terminal. From here it flows through the common circuit to the battery negative terminal.

This terminal will now be at a higher voltage or potential than the positive terminal, and the direction of current flow through the battery and the current consuming circuits will be reversed. This is indicated by the extinguishing of the warning lamp and the ammeter reading charge or positive.

Index